SCHOLASTIC COLLECTIONS

Compiled by Ian Souter

Stories to Read Aloud

© 1993 Scholastic Publications Ltd

Published by Scholastic Publications Ltd,
Villiers House,
Clarendon Avenue,
Leamington Spa,
Warwickshire CV32 5PR

Compiler Ian Souter
Editor Juliet Gladston
Series designer Joy White
Designer Anna Oliwa
Cover and illustrations Michael Terry

Designed using Aldus Pagemaker
Processed by Salvo Design and Print, Leamington Spa
Printed in Great Britain by Ebenezer Baylis & Son Ltd,
Worcester

British Library Cataloguing-in-Publication Data
A catalogue record for this book is
available from the British Library.

ISBN 0-590-53047-X

Contents

EARTH

LIVING THINGS

MY WORLD

ON THE MOVE

BACK IN TIME

JUST IMAGINE!

MAKING GOOD

Acknowledgements

The publishers gratefully acknowledge permission to reproduce the following copyright material:

Blackie Children's Books for 'The saver' © 1980 Nigel Hinton from *Beaver Towers*; Anderson Press Ltd for 'Time spinner' © 1990 Roy Apps from *Time Spinner*; © 1993 Moira Andrew for 'One long step'; © 1993 Steve Austin for 'Remembrance of things past'; Batsford Academic and Educational Ltd for 'Marna's paper bag' and 'The wonderful washing machine' © 1984 Linda Allen from *Stepping Stones*; BBC Publications for 'Charley and the machines' © Kathy Henderson, and 'Flying to India' and 'The dragonfly' © Libby Houston; Blackie & Son Ltd for 'Things are puzzling' © James Reeves from *Egg-Time Stories*; © 1993 Ann Bonner for 'King Winter' and 'The Edge'; © 1993 Alan Brown for 'I hate Mark and Gemma', 'Powder-monkey' and 'Summer magic'; © 1993 Stanley Cook for 'Paul the painter'; © 1993 Richard Cupidi for 'Earthmaker'; © 1993 Gill Davies for 'Sam's sky'; J M Dent & Sons Ltd for 'Green marmalade to you' © Margaret Mahy from *Nonstop Nonsense* and 'Eight hairy legs' © 1984 D H Wilson from *How to Stop a Train with One Finger*; © 1989 Gina Douthwaite for 'Charlotte's first hay-ride'; Faber & Faber Ltd for 'Dragon in Class 4' © June Counsel from *Dragon in Class 4*, Ginn & Co Ltd for 'The girl who changed the weather' © Alexander McCall Smith from *The Girl who Changed the Weather*; Victor Gollancz for 'Carrie's war' © 1973 Nina Bawden from *Carrie's War*; © 1993 Trevor Gorin for 'Remember the Fifth of November'; © 1993 David Harmer for 'Harriet's temper'; Harper Collins Publishers for 'The brave little toaster' © 1986 Thomas Disch from *The Brave Little Toaster*, 'Football revenge' © Julia Eccleshare from *Tobie and the Face Merchant*, 'Copy-cat friends' © 1991 Pratima Mitchell from *Stories for Six-Year-Olds* and 'The Christmas Tree Man' © Cynthia Rylant from *Silver Packages*; Hodder & Stoughton Ltd for 'James the Jumble' © Gill Davies from *James and the Jumble* and 'A candle in the dark' © Robert Swindells from *Candle in the Dark*; Jacaranda Wiley Ltd for 'Parker-Hamilton' © Robin Klein from *Ratbags and Rascals*; Kingfisher for 'Round the world with a tyre' © 1989 Edward Blishen from *A Treasury of Stories for Five-Year-Olds* by E and N Blishen and 'The King with dirty feet' © 1991 Pomme Clayton from *Time for Telling* compiled by Mary Medlicott; © 1993 Robin Mellor for 'The peanut butter princess'; © 1993 Polly Merchant for 'Canal family'; © 1993 Al Moir for 'The boy who stole the rainbow'; © 1993 Brian Moses for 'The burglary - different view points'; © 1993 Judith Nicholls for 'Remember, remember...'; Oxford University Press for 'Grandad's teeth' © Frank Flynn from *The Candy-Floss Tree*; Penguin Books Ltd for 'What we need is a new bus' © 1988 Jean Chapman from *Never Meddle with Magic and Other Stories* by Barbara Ireson, 'Raincloud' © 1988 Doris Harper-Wills from *Storyworld* compiled by Savior Pirotta (Blackie & Sons Ltd), 'London snow' © Paul Theroux from *London Snow* and 'A street of cats' © Rosemary Weir from *Pyewacket* (Blackie Children's Books); Random Century Group for 'The lonely skyscraper' © Jenny Hawkesworth from *Stuff and Nonsense* compiled by Laura Cecil (The Bodley Head), 'The hurricane tree' © Libby Purves from *Hurricane Tree* (The Bodley Head) and 'Thorkell Fairhair' © Henry Treece from *Viking Dawn* (The Bodley Head); © 1983 Merlin Price for 'Rescue'; © 1993 Ian Purnell for 'The treasure hunt'; Reed International Books for 'The chocolate touch' © Patrick Skene Catling from *The Chocolate Touch* (Methuen Childrens Books), 'Children of winter' © 1985 Berlie Doherty from *Children of Winter* (Methuen Childrens Books), 'The old man who sneezed' © Dorothy Edwards from *The Old Man who Sneezed* (Methuen Childrens Books), 'The brainbox' © Keren Kristal from *The Brainbox* (Methuen Childrens Books), 'Old Station' © Michael Morpurgo from *Conker* (William Heinemann Ltd), 'Hank Prank and the adenoids' © Jules Older from *Hank Prank and Hot Henrietta* (William Heinemann Ltd) and 'Adventures of Tom Sawyer' © Mark Twain from *Tom Sawyer* (Heinemann New Windmill Series, 1961); © 1993 John Rice for 'Dinosaur discovery'; Rogers, Coleridge and White for 'The last one off the ark' © 1993 Tony Bradman; Scholastic Childrens Books for 'Springtime for Toby' © 1987 Dorothy Joan Harris from *Four Seasons for Toby*, 'Rebecca's world' © Terry Nation from *Rebecca's World*, 'Badger's olympical games' © Emil Pacholek from *The Adventures of Badger's Set*, 'The boy and the swan' © 1987 Catherine Storr from *The Boy and the Swan* (Andre Deutsch) and 'When I lived down Cuckoo Lane...and came by tadpoles' © Jean Willis from *When I Lived Down Cuckoo Lane*; © Scholastic Publications Inc for 'That's nothing but junk, Josie' by Phyllis Rose Eisenberg, 'I would never choose a dragon for a pet' by Betty Lacey and 'Pollution!' by Helen Paladino from *Read Aloud Anthology* (Instructor Books); © 1993 Ian Souter for 'Hide and shriek', 'Red dragon' and 'Surrounded by bridges'; Viking/Kestrel Ltd for 'Dustbin Charlie' © 1988 Ann Pilling from *Dustbin Charlie*; Walker Books Ltd for 'Earthquake' © Ruskin Bond from *Earthquake*; Ward Lock Educational for 'The blue whale' © 1979 Frank Pinfold from *Primary School Assemblies*; © 1989 Irene Yates for 'I don't like this house!'; © 1993 Pauline Young for 'That's really flying'.

Every effort has been made to trace copyright holders. The publishers apologise for any inadvertent omissions.

EARTH

Sam's sky

'I'm going to paint the sky,' said Sam.

'That's nice,' said his mum, as Sam dipped his paintbrush into the jar of bright blue paint.

Sam painted a blue blue sky with a yellow sun all hot in the corner.

'What a lovely sky,' said his mum. 'It must be a nice sunny day in your picture.'

'Hey Sam, I like your sky,' said his sister Lucy, helping herself to a cake from the tin.

'That's a good sky,' said his dad. 'I wish the weather was as hot as that today.' It was raining outside, raining hard.

'I do like my sunny blue sky,' thought Sam. 'But I like the rain too....' So he swished his brush in the water jar and then put lots of raindrops and puddles on to the blue sky.

Sam liked his rainy sky but then... he thought of snow. Snow was even better. Sam splattered white flakes and swirls over the blue sky and across the wet rain.

'Sometimes,' thought Sam, 'it is foggy outside.' He found the grey paint and whirled his brush around and around over the blue sky and the sun and the rain and the snow.

'And sometimes,' thought Sam, 'there is thunder....'

He painted big black clouds over the blue and the sun and the rain and the snow and the fog. And then he added two great flashes of lightning across the blue and the sun and the rain and the snow and the fog and the thunder.

Sam sighed happily. His picture was finished.

'Do you like my sky?' asked Sam, when his sister Lucy came in to take another cake.

'No,' said Lucy. 'It looks a mess.'

Sam was sad.

'Do you like my sky, Dad?' he asked.

'I don't know,' said Dad. 'I think I liked the sunny one better.'

So Sam was even sadder.

'Why did you spoil it, Sam?' asked Lucy, eating another cake. 'It's a shame'.

And Sam was sadder still.

Just then Mum came into the room.

'I like your picture, Sam,' she said.

Sam smiled.

'What are those white bits?' she asked.

'That's lightning,' Sam told her... 'and there's the thunder, and the fog, and the snow, and the rain, and the sun and the blue.'

'What a wonderful idea!' said Mum. 'You've painted all the weather at once. Aren't you clever, Sam!'

And she pinned the picture up on the notice-board for everyone to see. And Sam felt very happy.

Then they all had tea, but no cakes, because Lucy had eaten them all.

Gill Davies

Raincloud

In the beginning, no one lived on Earth. Everybody lived in the Land of Sky. Birds flew in the blue of Sky. Snakes crawled in the clouds of Sky. Even fish swam in the sea of Sky.

One day, a boy called Okonorote went out hunting in the clouds. He was looking for Magic Bird – the bird with the rainbow feathers.

Okonorote travelled far from home. He looked in the valleys. He searched on the hills. At last he saw a silver tree. On top of the tree was a nest. And sitting in the nest was Magic Bird.

Okonorote took aim. Zwing. Zwing. His arrows left the bow. Swish. Swish. Their sharp heads travelled through the air. Tang. One arrow hit Magic Bird.

'Haiee,' Okonorote shouted happily. 'I have caught the Magic Bird.'

The young hunter ran to the silver tree. But the bird was nowhere in sight. Okonorote looked around. In the ground there was a big, gaping hole. Magic Bird had fallen through it.

Okonorote looked down the hole. Far below he saw Magic Bird lying on a green land. Okonorote gasped. 'Land,' he shouted. 'Land down below.'

People came running out of their cloud-houses to see. 'Land down below,' they all gasped. 'Land down below.'

Quickly, Okonorote made a rope ladder out of hemp and twine. Down, down, down he went. Past the galaxies and the meteors. Past the sun and the stars. Right through the winds and the rainbows. Soon he touched the rocks of Earth.

Okonorote looked around him. The Magic Bird was lying on the ground. Okonorote ran to pick it up. But the bird disappeared. Instead of it, there was a tiny hill. As Okonorote watched, the hill grew into a mountain.

'Look,' said the people in the sky. 'Okonorote has built a mountain to help us down.'

One after the other the Sky People climbed down to Earth. They looked around them and saw the green grass,

the yellow sunshine and the brown soil.

'How warm it is down here,' they said. 'Let us stay here'.

Soon, everyone had left the cold Land of Sky. Everyone, that is, except a little girl who was too scared to climb down the ladder. The girl's name was Raincloud.

Okonorote saw Raincloud peeping out of the hole in the sky. 'Don't be afraid,' he called. 'Climb down.'

Carefully, Raincloud put her left foot on the ladder. The ladder swung dangerously. Raincloud stepped back. She waited a moment. Then she tried again. This time she kept her eyes closed.

Slowly Raincloud climbed down past the sun. She stepped over the moon. At last she reached the rainbow.

'How warm it is down here,' said Raincloud to herself. And she opened her eyes to see. Almost immediately, she felt dizzy. The land below looked very far away. Raincloud's feet started to slip.

'Don't move,' shouted Okonorote. Quickly, he scampered up the ladder.

'One, two, three, four, five....' The people started to count the rungs.

Suddenly there was a loud snap. The rope broke in two. Okonorote fell back to Earth. Raincloud was left clinging to a rock-

cloud in the sky. 'Help,' she called.

Okonorote climbed to the top of a tall tree.

'Jump,' he called. 'Raincloud, jump.'

But Raincloud was too scared to do anything. She just sat on the rock-cloud and cried. Slowly, the cloud started to drift away. Soon Raincloud could not see her friends any more.

The sun set and the moon came out. Raincloud was so tired she went to sleep. When she woke up again, she was floating above the sea. Raincloud saw a dolphin and a shark, and a baby whale trailing after its mother.

'What a beautiful place Earth is,' thought Raincloud. 'Some day soon I'm going to find the courage to jump off this rock-cloud. Then I'll join my friends in the New World.'

But time passed, and Raincloud stayed where she was. Her friends built houses and roads and became the first Earth People. They forgot all about Raincloud waiting in the Sky.

The poor girl is still sitting up there to this very day, trying to find enough courage to jump to Earth. Sometimes she gets so lonely, she starts to cry.

Then her tears fall on the people below.

Retold by Doris Harper-Wills

Springtime for Toby

Toby Turtle sat on a rock in the farm pond. All the other young turtles were there too. They were listening to Grandma Turtle tell stories about the pond, and about the seasons that were coming.

'Winter is past,' she told them. 'The sun is warming our rock now. Spring and summer are coming to our pond, and autumn too. There will be many, many new things for you young turtles to see.'

'What sort of things?' asked one of the turtles.

'Lovely things. Pussywillows and flowers, birds and butterflies, juicy berries and chestnuts, new grass and bright autumn leaves.'

'Oh,' said Toby, his eyes wide with wonder, 'will I see all that?'

'Yes,' said Grandma Turtle. 'In a little while spring will be here.'

'But when?' asked Toby. 'When will spring come? When will all that start to happen?'

'Soon,' said Grandma Turtle. 'Just wait.'

But Toby did not like waiting for anything. He wanted to see all those interesting things right away.

'I won't wait for spring to come to our pond,' he said to himself. 'I will go and look for it.'

So Toby left his rock and set off to find spring. Since he had never been away from his pond before, he wasn't sure where to start looking.

'I will follow this fence,' he decided. 'That way I won't get lost, and when I've found spring I'll know how to get back to the pond.'

Toby began to plod his way along the fence. Turtles walk very, *very* slowly. By the time night came he had passed only three fence posts. But Toby wasn't worried. He pulled his head and legs into his shell and slept right where he was.

The next morning he set off again and went past another three fence posts. He did that for several days.

'It's taking a long time to find spring,' he thought to himself. 'I wonder if I'm looking in the right place.'

Just then Toby heard someone calling him.

'Hallo,' said a small striped animal. 'Who are you?'

'I'm Toby,' he answered. 'Toby Turtle.'

'Oh,' said the striped animal. 'A turtle, eh? I'm a chipmunk. What are you doing here? Turtles don't usually come to the meadow.'

'I'm looking for spring,' said Toby.

'Spring?' said the chipmunk. 'Well then – just look around. There are new leaves on the trees and the grass is turning green. The robins are back and their nests are full of baby birds. The crocuses and pussywillows are out, and over by the farmhouse you can see the farmer's children skipping. All these things are part of spring.'

'Oh,' said Toby, 'then I've found spring!'

The chipmunk scurried off. Toby looked around at all the signs of spring. He ate some tender green grass and sniffed at a white snowdrop and listened to the robins singing overhead.

'Spring *is* nice,' he said to himself. 'Grandma Turtle was right. But I wonder... I wonder if summer is just as nice.' Toby bit off some more grass and thought about that. 'Maybe... maybe if I keep going I'll find summer too.'

Dorothy Joan Harris

The hurricane tree

Once upon a time there was a boy called William, who lived in an old house underneath a tall tree.

In the spring the tree was like a big pale green umbrella, higher than the roof-top, and if William looked up into the branches, he could see birds building their nests.

In the summer, he had his lunch under the tree, then leaned on its smooth warm trunk and fed the crumbs to the squirrels.

In the autumn, the tree dropped sticky prickly beech-nuts into William's sand-pit, and threw down heaps of dry golden leaves. He made beds out of them, and mountains, and kicked them into snowstorms.

And in the winter, when the real snow came, his mummy sometimes took him to the kitchen window at bedtime, to see the big yellow moon through the top of the tree. 'It looks like a balloon tangled up in the branches,' said William. 'One day, when I'm big, I'm going to climb right up that tree and sit next to a bird's nest and look at the stars.'

'It's a very old tree,' said William's daddy. 'It's more than a hundred years old. Someone must have planted it in the old days, and looked after it to help it grow straight and strong.'

'What was it like in the old days?' said William.

'Well,' said his daddy, 'I wasn't even born then, so I don't remember. But when that tree was a new shoot, there weren't any cars, or aeroplanes, or tractors. Big brown horses worked on the land instead, pulling ploughs and carts. And the people didn't have electricity, either. They cooked their food on wood fires.'

'Just like a barbeque,' said William.

'They didn't have electric lights, either,' said his mummy. 'The children had candles to light them to bed.'

But one night, very late, William woke up feeling a bit frightened. A wind was blowing outside, a very strong wind indeed. He could hear the tiles rattling on the roof, and the trees sighing and creaking. The noise made him sad. He climbed out of bed and went to the window, but everything was black outside, because there was no moon. He couldn't see the garden, and he couldn't see the tree. Something went CRASH! in the dark, and his little sister Lucy started to cry in her sleep. William had to keep his eyes shut, so he didn't cry too.

Suddenly his daddy came in with a torch in his hand, making big black shadows on the wall. 'The electricity isn't working. I think the wind must have blown the wires down. But we can see all right with the torch. You two can come into bed with Mummy and me.'

William tried to sleep in the big bed, but the wind was still howling around the house and whistling in the chimney-pots, and he kept thinking about the birds in the tall tree branches. 'Will they be all right in the wind?' he asked. But his mummy and daddy were asleep. Once he thought he heard a cracking sound, and a sigh, out in the garden. Then he went to sleep too.

In the morning, the family came downstairs and looked out of the window. 'Oh!' they all shouted together. The big beech tree was down. The wind had knocked it right over in the night. You could see its roots tipped up against the sky, and even the very top branches were lying on the ground, in the mud by the garden gate. And all the secret shadows had gone from the garden.

William began to cry. 'You said it took a hundred years to grow that tree!' he sobbed. 'But people don't live as long as that. I will be dead before it can grow up again so beautiful.'

He wouldn't eat his breakfast, and he wouldn't play with his toys. He didn't even care when Lucy borrowed his best clockwork train. Daddy said that William could help to put some tiles back on the roof, but William said, 'No. I don't want to do anything. I want my tree to stand up again.'

'Well it can't,' said Daddy. He went off to fix the roof, and William just stood and looked at the poor old tree.

After a while William said, 'May I climb on it?'

'Yes,' said Daddy. And he helped him up. William sat on the trunk and held on to a high branch. 'I'm a squirrel,' he said. Daddy lifted up Lucy to be another squirrel next to him. 'Have a nut,' said William kindly, and Lucy ate a pretend nut. Then William climbed further along the tree-trunk, and found a higher branch to sit on. It felt safe and secret, up among the leaves. 'The tree is still my friend,' he said.

Libby Purves

The girl who changed the weather

It was tucked away in the darkest of the corners and, at first, Emily was not sure what it was. She picked up a piece of cloth and dusted it. As the grime disappeared, she began to see the outlines of a map. Then she noticed a box at the bottom which was filled with symbols. There were pictures of clouds and pictures of the sun. There were black dots and lightning shapes and white, fluffy pictures made out of cotton wool.

'It's an old weather map,' Emily said to herself. She dragged the map out from its hiding place and looked at it more closely. Now that it was in the light, she thought that she recognised it. It was the map the weather forecaster before Mr Wells had used to show people what weather to expect. Every evening after the news, the forecaster would stand in front of his map and put signs on it. If it was going to be rainy the following day, he would put on black dots. If it was going to be sunny, he would stick on a picture of the sun.

Mr Wells had a new weather map now – one which was controlled by a computer – and so they had put this old one away in the storeroom. Emily felt that it was a bit of a pity; it must have been fun to stick the symbols on the map. She picked up a few and stuck them in position. Then she turned and faced an imaginary camera. 'Not a very good day tomorrow,' she said, pointing to the rainy symbols. 'But it should clear up later, with any luck. So you can all expect a sunny afternoon.'

She smiled, deciding that she could really be quite good at presenting the weather forecast. If Mr Wells ever decided to do something else, well then perhaps she could apply for his job.

She grinned at her imaginary camera. 'And that's all from the weather department,' she announced. 'Good-night!'

It was almost a week before Emily saw the weather map again. That Monday, her father was working late and so Emily had more time to spend at the station than usual. She went into the storeroom, thinking that she might try out some of the old costumes she had discoverd, but then she saw the weather map and decided to make another weather forecast.

She raked through the box of symbols. Right at the bottom, underneath a pile of spare rain clouds, there were several pictures of strong winds. These were thick, black arrows, which looked just like winds would look if you had to draw them. She took these out, dusted them, and prepared to stick them on.

'Very windy tonight,' she said. 'Gales from the west, getting stronger all night. If you're a sailor, keep on shore! If your roof is loose, look out!'

She stuck the windy symbols on the map, looking very serious as she did so. 'The winds will last until about nine o'clock tomorrow morning,' she announced. 'Then they will drop and the rest of the day will be fine.' She smiled. 'And that's the end of the weather forecast.'

Emily looked at the map with its windy symbols. If that were the real weather forecast, she would not like to be out and about.

Her father finished his work,

switched off his camera, and came out to meet Emily in the hall. They said good-night to Mr Rufus and drove off home, stopping, of course, at the ice-cream parlour on the way. Once at home, Emily's father made her favourite meal of sausages and beans, which they sat down to eat in the kitchen.

Afterwards, standing at the kitchen sink, doing the washing up, Emily's father looked out of the window into the dark of the night.

'There's a wind coming up,' he said. 'Listen.'

Emily listened. A gust pushed against the window pane, making it rattle. 'Maybe there's a storm on its way,' she said.

'Yes,' said her father. 'I think I'll put the car in the garage tonight.'

When the washing up was finished, Emily said good-night to her father and went off to her bedroom. She was tired, and it was pleasant to snuggle down into her warm bed and listen to the sound of the rising wind outside. It was like the sound of the sea crashing against the rocks and it made her feel drowsy to listen to it.

At six o'clock the next morning, Emily awoke to the sound of a gale. It was a high-pitched, whining sound, whipping round the house, wailing down the chimney. Emily looked out of her window to see the tree-tops waving to and fro and the tops of hedges flattened by the wind. She wondered how the branches of the trees could stand the blast without breaking, and what the poor birds would think. It must surely be impossible to fly against such a wind, she thought.

'Gales,' said her father over the breakfast table. 'Force eight gales.'

Emily ate her breakfast and prepared for school. Then, with her hat firmly pushed down over her head, she went to catch her bus. It was as much as she could do to keep on her feet, so strong were the winds and, as for the bus, it was an effort for the driver to keep it going in a straight line.

At school, the wind had wreaked havoc in the playground. Benches were overturned and pieces of paper were scattered all over. There were even hats and caps caught against fences, having been lifted off the heads of unwary people. What was strangest of all, though, and very funny, was the pair of pants which had been blown up to the top of the flagpole and caught there. Now they fluttered in the wind, just like an ordinary flag.

Then, precisely at nine o'clock, the wind dropped. There were a few more puffs and then complete stillness. The sky, which had been overcast, now became blue and sunny. It was as if the weather was trying to apologise for behaving so badly in the night.

'How strange,' thought Emily. 'One moment it's blowing a gale and the next it's as still as a midsummer day.'

She gazed out of the window, watching the sun emerge from behind the last of the clouds. Then she looked at her watch and an extraordinary thought struck her. Nine o'clock. 'It's exactly as I predicted,' she said to herself. 'It's exactly what I put on the weather map.'

It was, of course, no more than a coincidence.

'There's no other explanation,' Emily muttered under her breath. 'It's just pure chance.'

Alexander McCall Smith

The king with dirty feet

Once upon a time there was a king. He lived in a hot, dusty village in India. He had everything he wanted and was very happy. But there was one thing that this king hated and that was bathtime.

Perhaps he was a little bit like you?

This king had not washed for a week, he had not washed for a month, he had not washed for a whole year. He had begun to smell. He smelt underneath his arms, in between his toes, behind his ears and up his nose. He was the smelliest king there has ever been. His servants were all very polite about it, but nobody liked to be in the same room as him. Until one day the smell became too much for even the king himself, and he said rather sadly, 'I think it is time I had a bath.'

He walked slowly down to the river. The villagers whispered, 'The king's going to have a bath!' and they rushed down to the river bank to get the best view.

Everyone fell silent when the king stepped into the cool, clear river water. When he called for the royal soap, a huge cheer arose. He washed himself from top to bottom, scrubbed his hair and brushed his teeth. He played with his little toy ducks and his little boat.

Then, at last, when he was quite clean, he called for the royal towel and stepped out of the river.

When he had finished drying himself he saw that his feet were covered with dust.

'Oh bother,' he cried. 'I forgot to wash them.' So he stepped back into the water and soaped them well. But as soon as he stood on dry land his feet were dirty again.

'Oh my goodness,' he said crossly. 'I didn't wash them well enough. Bring me a scrubbing brush.' The king scrubbed his feet until they shone. But still, when he stepped on the ground they were dirty.

This time the king was furious. He shouted for his servant, Gabu. Gabu came running and bowed low before the king.

'Gabu,' boomed the king, 'the king has had a bath, the king is clean, but the earth is dirty. There is dust everywhere. You must clean the earth so there is no more dust and my feet stay clean.'

'Yes, Your Majesty,' replied Gabu.

'You have three days in which to rid the land of dust, and if you fail do

you know what will happen to you?' asked the king.

'No, Your Majesty.'

'ZUT!' cried the king.

'ZUT?' said Gabu. 'What is ZUT?'

'ZUT is the sound of your head being chopped off.'

Gabu began to cry.

'Don't waste time, Gabu. Rid the land of dust at once.'

The king marched back to his palace.

'I must put my thinking cap on,' said Gabu, and he put his head in his hands and began to think.

'When something is dirty, you brush it.'

He asked the villagers to help him. They took their brushes and brooms and ONE... TWO... THREE....

They all began to sweep – swish, swish, swish, swish – all day long.

Until the dust rose up and filled the air in a thick, dark cloud. Everyone was coughing and spluttering and bumping into each other. The king choked, 'Gabu, where are you? I asked you to rid the land of dust, not fill the air with dust. Gabu, you have two more days and ZUT!'

'Oh dear, oh dear,' cried Gabu, and put his head in his hands and thought.

'When something is dirty, you wash it.'

He asked all the villagers to help him. They took their buckets to the well and filled them up to the brims with water and ONE... TWO... THREE....

They all began to pour – sloosh, sloosh, sloosh, sloosh – all day long.

There was so much water it spread across the land. It began to rise. Soon it was up to their ankles, their knees, their waists and then up to their chests.

'Swim everybody,' cried Gabu.

The king climbed on to the top of the highest mountain where the water lapped his toes and he sniffed, 'Gabu, a...atchoo! Where are you?'

Gabu came swimming.

'Yes, Your Majesty?'

'Gabu, I asked you to rid the land of dust not turn our village into a swimming pool. You have one more day and ZUT!'

'Oh dear, oh dear, I have run out of ideas,' cried Gabu. The water trickled away and Gabu put his head in his hands and thought.

'I could put the king in an iron room with no windows or doors, chinks or cracks, then no speck of dust could creep in. But I don't think he would like that. Oh, if only I could cover up all the dust with a carpet.' Then Gabu had a marvellous idea.

'Of course, why didn't I think of this before? Everyone has a needle and thread and a little piece of leather. Leather is tough, we will cover the land with leather.'

He asked the villagers to help him. Needles were threaded and knots were tied and ONE... TWO... THREE....

They all began to sew – stitch, stitch, stitch, stitch – all day long.

Then the huge piece of leather was spread across the land and it fitted perfectly. It stretched from the school to the well, from the temple to the palace, and all the way down to the river.

'We've done it,' cried Gabu. 'I will go and tell the king.'

Gabu knocked on the palace door.

'We are ready, Your Majesty.'

The king poked his head carefully around the door not knowing what to expect. Then a little smile twitched at the corners of his mouth. The ground looked clean, very clean indeed. He put one foot on the leather and it was spotless. The king walked across the leather.

'This is splendid, comfortable, clean. Well done, Gabu. Well done.'

The king turned to the villagers to thank them.

Suddenly out of the crowd stepped a little old man with a long white beard and a bent back. Everyone had forgotten him. He bowed low before the king and spoke in a very quiet voice.

'Your Majesty, how will anything be able to grow now that the land is covered with leather? The grass will not be able to push its way through. There will be no vegetables or flowers and no new trees. The animals will be hungry and there will be nothing for us to eat.'

Now everyone was listening.

'Your Majesty, you know you don't have to cover the land with leather to keep your feet clean. It is really quite simple.'

The old man took out of his pocket a large pair of scissors. He bent down and began to cut the leather very carefully all around the king's feet. Then he took two laces from his pocket and tied each piece of leather to the king's feet. Then he pulled back the leather that covered the earth and said, 'Try them, Your Majesty.'

The king looked down at his feet covered in leather and frowned. He had never seen anything like it. He put one foot forward.

'Mmm, very good!' he exclaimed. He took another step. 'This is splendid, comfortable, clean *and* the grass can grow!'

Then the king walked, then he ran and then he jumped.

'Hooray,' he cried. 'I can walk here, and here, and here. I can walk anywhere and my feet will always be clean.'

What was the king wearing on his feet?

That's right, he was wearing SHOES!

They were the first pair of shoes ever to be made, and people have been wearing them ever since.

Pomme Clayton

Earthquake

Grandfather and Mukesh found themselves on top of the struggling shopkeeper. As he freed himself, Mukesh got stuck in the awning and had to be helped out, and all the time the ground was heaving about and shops were tottering and collapsing like packs of cards.

In the space of a few seconds, a straight bazaar had become a crooked bazaar. The road had been twisted out of shape to such an extent that some shops that had been on the left now turned up on the right, and vice versa. A beggar in a cart who had never been known to walk now leapt to his feet and ran for his life. The cows had vanished and so had the policemen. A motorcycle had disappeared into a hole in the ground, while a car had mounted the steps of the town hall. A tonga-pony galloped down the middle of the road; of the tonga and its driver there was no sign.

The town hall itself had collapsed, burying a number of clerks and officials. By the time the powerful tremor had passed, several other large buildings had also come down.

Grandfather did not panic. He picked Mukesh off a heap of sweets and helped the dazed shopkeeper to his feet. Then he realised that the earthquake must have affected every part of the town.

'Let's get back to the house,' he said.

'Anything could have happened!'

Grabbing Mukesh by the hand, he started running down the road. Mukesh had trouble keeping up with him. He'd never seen Grandfather running before.

Dolly was helping Grandmother hang out the washing when the shock came. Had they been inside the house, they would not have come out alive.

As in the case of the first tremor, the dog began to howl and all the birds rose from the trees and began circling overhead, making a great noise. Then suddenly there was a wind rushing through the trees, and the ground began to heave and quake.

Dolly looked up to see the tall chimney toppling off the roof of the house.

'Look, Granny!' she cried. 'The house is falling down! What will happen to my doll's house?'

'Never mind the doll's house,' said Grandmother. 'Let's get clear of the building.'

They ran into the garden just as the walls of the house bulged outwards and the roof fell inwards. There was a great crash, followed by clouds of dust and plaster.

Grandmother looked across the road and saw other houses collapsing, almost as though some unseen giant was blowing them all down. The lines from an English fairy-tale ran through her head. 'I'll huff and I'll puff and I'll blow your house down!'

There was a peculiar whistling wind, but it wasn't wind that had done the damage; it was the quivering of the earth that had loosened bricks and plaster, beams and rafters. The air was filled with choking dust. They couldn't speak.

How flimsy all the houses seem, thought Grandmother. Just dolls' houses. And yet, many of them had stood for over a hundred years. A hundred years – and in a moment, gone!

The shaking had stopped, but already their home was a mound of rubble. A bedstead poked out of a broken window. A bathroom tap gushed water over a squashed sofa. Here a bit of broken desk or chair, there a bit of torn carpet, a familiar hat, battered books, a twisted umbrella; these were the only reminders that this had once been a home.

The goat was missing, the hens had vanished. The only things that hadn't been touched were the clothes that Dolly and Grandmother had been hanging up. They remained firmly on the washing-line, flapping about in the wind.

Cries from afar came to them on the wind – cries for help, people calling out for each other, some just shouting because there was nothing else to do.

Dolly and Grandmother stood like statues in the middle of the garden. They were too shocked to move – until they saw Grandfather and Mukesh running down the road towards them. Then they too began to run.

Pickle found himself trapped in the store-room. He had been ferreting between two large boxes, trying to get at a terrified rat, when the ceiling came down on top of the two boxes. There was dust and darkness everywhere. Pickle didn't like it one bit. He wanted to be out of that suffocating hole, and he wasn't going to sit there, waiting to be rescued. The instincts of the dachshund, and his own experience in digging for rats, now came to his aid. He began burrowing in the rubble, trying to tunnel a way out.

Ruskin Bond

King Winter

There was a Giant Winter
Came to a northern land
Cast his spell upon it
Ruled with an iron hand.

Worked his silent magic
Covered all with snow
Banished the sun forever
Forbade the corn to grow.

So a terrible famine
Struck the people there
No harvest to be gathered
Cupboards, tables, bare.

Fires gave no comfort
Hearths were cold as stone
In the bitter wilderness
Land lay hard, like bone.

Winter sent the people
Into a slumber deep
Motionless and rigid
All were lost in sleep.

One did keep a vigil
Through the frozen night
Watching for the sunrise
Waiting for some light.

Then at last he saw it
A brilliant, shining star
Which led him on a journey
When he travelled far.

From the barren snowfields
Searching for the sun
To a distant country
Where spring had just begun.

Birds were singing gladly
Crops were growing green
There it was he found her
Summer's gentle Queen.

When she heard his story
She agreed to go
To reason with the Giant
King of winter's snow.

Summer spoke to Winter
With her every breath
The giant lost his power
Relaxed his grip of death.

Southern winds blew softly
Summoned by the Queen
Winter's snow was melted
The land again was green.

People woke and marvelled
At the sky of blue
The giant was defeated
The giant then withdrew.

When the day is darkest
And perished is the cold
Think of summer's sunshine
Think of summer's gold.

The Giant visits only
For few months of the year
However hard the winter
The Queen is always near.

Ann Bonner

London snow

The morning for the children was like no other morning they had known. There were no city noises – not even dogs. No planes, no cars, no trains. There had been times when a motor launch on the river would hoot in the early morning as it passed Saint Mary's and The Old Swan. There were no hoots. And the sky was still. It was as if London were holding its breath.

Wallace opened his eyes. It was dark in the hall; his nose was very cold. Mrs Mutterance looked at her alarm clock – it was just past eight! Amy woke without moving, hearing Mrs Mutterance cry, 'My bedsocks are rucked!'

Then Amy saw the street-lamps of Church Road – their yellow froth in the grey air. And there was another colour: it was an eerie blue fluorescence, and when she looked again she saw a gigantic line of laundry, like sheets on a rope, hanging over Vicarage Crescent. She heard the clank of milk bottles – that was odd, because she had not heard the engine of the milk van. Why was the milkman walking, and why didn't his footsteps make sound?

'What's wrong, Ma?' asked Wallace.

Mrs Mutterance was in her dressing gown and red bedsocks. She wore her fingerless mittens and she was standing at the kitchen door clawing gently at her scalp.

'I've got something on my mind,' she said. 'Just now I thought I was ten years old. I was Trood.'

Wallace began to laugh. He had a growling laugh, and he shut his eyes and nodded as the laughter rolled out of him.

'That's what my father called me – Trood. He gave me gob-stoppers from the shop. I used to slide down the hill near the flats on a tea-tray. I must have been ten – to get myself on to a tea tray.'

It was the morning that made her think of it. She had not known a morning like this for fifty years. It was the silence and the snow, and the cold, too. It was dry; there was no dampness in it, and no wind; just the still white scarf of winter.

Wallace said,' I dreamed that London was made out of cloth.'

Amy said, 'I can see laundry everywhere!'

Wallace said, 'Cottonwool!'

It was snow.

It clung thickly to the roof-tops where it was nearly blue. It was mounded like white eyebrows above the windows of the houses, and it had blown against the brick walls and stuck, making beards hang from the sills. It was piled against the doors and made caps on the tops of lamp-posts. Each spike on the churchyard fence was encased in a fluffy sheath, and so far the only marks in the white street – what a beautiful street it seemed! – were the milkman's footprints.

Mrs Mutterance, Wallace and little Amy stood at the front window, above the shop and marvelled. The city had a new shape, very soft contours and different colours. It was hardly a city. The Chelsea Flour Mill across the river had become a snowy mountain, and behind it was a landscape of larger and smaller hills. It was as if, in the night, the city had been removed and in its place an empty countryside of simple hills had appeared.

Saint Mary's seemed a country church, banked by snow, at the edge of a snowy meadow where lambs nestled. But the meadow was the frozen river on which the snow had settled, and some icy wavelets had produced the illusion of lambs. The city was simplified. It was perfectly dry and white. And this, Mrs Mutterance said, was what had woken them in the night: the covering of snow had shut out every sound, stopped the trains, grounded the planes, kept everyone indoors. Even now, in the morning, there was no movement. The city lay frozen and very still. The birds were gone, there were no voices, the sky was empty. The nearer warehouses were mountainous and their chutes were like ski-slopes. The wreckage on the patch of waste ground near Westover Road was gone, and in its place were bulging igloos and whitened statuary. The window panes were feathery from the flakes that had stuck to them, and from every eave and drainpipe hung icicle daggers and the loveliest swords of ice.

'Why is it so quiet, Ma?' asked Amy.

'The snow's stopped the yip-yap,' said Mrs Mutterance. 'It's a kind of clogulation – it just came down and snuffled everything. Gosh, ain't it pretty?'

'It's all smothered up,' said Wallace.

'But where's the river, Ma?'

'It's not on top any more,' said Mrs Mutterance. 'My guess is that it's underneath.'

There was no traffic on the river. They were used to seeing it as black and spiky at high tide, grey and swift at low tide, churning in all directions when the tide was rising. Rowers in narrow skiffs often slid along the river, like water insects. The river had enlarged the city by mirroring it, but now its size had diminished. There were no reflections, only an even whiteness which matched the silence. The wet black city was gone.

'There's a house on top, where the river should be,' said Wallace.

It was the lighter, transformed to a shed. It did not bob, and the snow had drifted round it. Its bow was covered, its portholes at the level of the snow, and the drum on which it was moored was hidden. Closer, the masts on the Thames sailing barges at Saint Mary's embankment were like frozen trees.

Amy said, 'It's magic.'

'No,' said Mrs Mutterance, 'it's about as normal as it could be. Normal and thermal. But take a good look now, because pretty soon it will waterfy and go down the drains. You know, this is what London was like when I was a girl, and we had silver sixpences in the Christmas pud. Goodness, it takes me back! I had my own tea-tray, for sliding. My father gave me glacier mints and called me Trood.'

She spoke dreamily: she had recovered her happiness. Wallace said, 'I'm glad there's no school. We can get some tea-trays and go sliding.'

Paul Theroux

Summer magic

I don't know if it was Isaac who found the summer magic, or Beanpole. Isaac's the brainy one – we call him Isaac Newton and drop apples on his head – but Beanpole, she gives ideas to the gang.

'Seaside and ice-cream,' said Dazzer, 'down on the beach.'

We looked out the window of Isaac's garden shed. Winter rain rippled across the glass so that all we could see was wavy underwater reflections of the leafless trees in the garden. A cold wind rattled the door and blew round our legs where we sat on a pile of old potato sacks. Summer couldn't have been further away.

'The sun's so hot I can feel it on my face,' said Beanpole.

Isaac rocked to and fro, his little flipper arms clasped round his knees. 'When I close my eyes,' he chanted in a solemn voice, 'when I close my eyes really tight – I can hear the sea.'

We all screwed our eyes up really tight, and Isaac was right. We could hear the sea.

'And the gulls,' I said, listening to their mewling cries as they swooped and soared in the wake of the fishing boats.

'Let me show you the seaside,' said Beanpole, getting to her feet. There was magic in the air, an electric, tingly feeling that made your hair sprout and goosebumps grow on your arms. Magic, summer magic, took us out of Isaac's shed, out of the wind and the rain and the cold, away from the dark days of winter, and into the bright sunshine of summer.

We followed her slowly down the promenade; slowly because Isaac can't walk very fast, slowly because we wanted to stop and look in every shop and every arcade that we passed, slowly because it was so hot!

There were shops selling buckets and spades and nets with big holes that never catch anything. There were shops selling water-wings and Lilos and camping gas and suntan lotions. There were shops selling doughnuts and candy-floss and hamburgers and cockles and mussels and fish and chips. The smell of food made my mouth water.

And of course there was a shop selling ice-cream, in twenty different flavours.

'I haven't got any money!' Dazzer sounded as if he'd just crushed his fingers in a door. I felt around in my pockets and found some coins that had slipped through a hole and into the lining. With all our money we bought two ice-creams. I shared a tutti-frutti with Isaac, and Dazzer and Beanpole had a rum and raisin.

So when we got to the amusement arcade we could only stand and watch – the flashing lights and flickering screens, the players tense over their steering wheels and joysticks, music pounding so loud you feel it through your feet.

We stumbled down on to the bench in a daze and took off our shoes and socks.

'This is the life,' said Beanpole, squishing sand between her toes.

We ran up and down the sand with Beanpole and me carrying Isaac in a sling we made with our arms. We slid through the dry stuff at the top of the beach, leaving people shouting at our backs as they shook sand from their hair. We pounded along at the water's edge, zigzagging in and out of the water. We ran between the volley-ball players who fell over each other in confusion. We leaped over sand-castles that cracked and crumbled from the thunder of our feet.

'I'm hot,' Isaac complained.

'You're hot?' Beanpole panted. 'We should be hot. We're carrying you.'

'It's all this sun,' said Isaac. 'I wish I had your black skin. I need a swim.'

We weren't prepared for summer magic. We swam in our pants and vests alongside others in smart swimming costumes. Isaac loved the water, swimming strongly on his back into the waves.

'I should have been a fish,' he said. 'I would have made a good fish.'

The water was warm and swirly. When we came out we buried Isaac up to his neck in the sand, and then he had to go in the sea again to wash the sand off. We lay in the sun until we were dry.

'That was amazing,' said Dazzer, back in Isaac's garden shed in the cold wind and rain.

'That was magic,' said Isaac.

I got to my feet, summer magic fluttering in my stomach. 'Let me show you how we know it's summer.'

We walked through the town together. People were standing outside the pubs, drinking and chatting.

'It's late, but it's still light,' said Isaac.

'And still warm,' said Dazzer.

'That's why I'm wearing shorts and my T-shirt,' I said. 'Look! We're like bright birds!'

On a street corner tables spilled out of a café across the pavement. Diners sat eating, some drinking wine slowly and thoughtfully, others talking loudly with much waving of knife and fork.

'It's just like abroad,' said Beanpole.

We turned the corner and were instantly swept up in a carnival. Men in dark suits were carrying giant figures of saints. Children in fancy costumes rode on lorries covered with deep banks of flowers of every colour and fragrance, brass bands marched to their own loud music, and the crowd danced to the sound of flamenco guitars.

'It's Spain!' yelled Dazzer. 'We were there last year!'

We danced until our feet were sore from stamping and our fingers stiff from clicking. Isaac danced with one brightly plumed lady after another. They swung him round till he was dizzy and nearly fainting with excitement.

When we could dance no more we all flopped down on the ground and were back in Isaac's shed.

'Wild!' Isaac groaned.

'More summer magic,' said Beanpole. 'We can all do it.'

Dazzer stood up. 'Let me show you what I do in summer.'

He led us to the park where men in white were playing cricket.

'Dazzer!' they shouted. 'We're short of players. Bring your friends and help out.'

Play started. Dazzer bowled.

'Wide!' called Isaac, who'd been asked to umpire. His eyes were quicker and sharper than anybody's.

Dazzer bowled again. Crack! The batsman hit the ball a tremendous whack and it came hurtling towards where I was fielding with Beanpole. I ran for it. She ran for it. We collided and collapsed in a heap of giggles and the ball ran on past us and hit the boundary fence with a clunk.

'Four!'

At lunch we sat on the pavilion veranda, eating sandwiches and strawberries and cream and drinking lemonade.

When I felt too full to move and just a bit sick, Dazzer dragged us to our feet and on to the tennis courts.

'I'll play the lot of you,' he said.

That's just what he did, running this way and that, whack, whack. He was as good as anybody you see at Wimbledon, though I don't know who won because I can't keep score at tennis.

We were exhausted, and lay on our

backs in the park, smelling the new-mown grass, the sun beating pinkly through our closed eyelids.

'You're magic at games, Dazzer,' said Beanpole.

Perhaps I was jealous of all the attention Dazzer was getting. Anyway, I started to moan.

'I get bored in summer. There's so much of it that I start to wish I was back at school.'

The spell was broken and we opened our eyes to find ourselves back in Isaac's shed.

'You spoiled it!' Dazzer complained. 'Just because I beat you at tennis.'

'You didn't beat us. It was a draw.' I didn't really have a clue but I had to say something.

'A draw! You don't have a draw at tennis. That just shows how much you know. You just can't play for toffee....'

'I can play better than you....'

'Hang on you two!' It was Isaac coming between us. 'Stop your arguing or you will spoil everything.'

I was pleased to stop, but Dazzer made a face. He knew he was winning.

'Let me show you my summer,' said Isaac.

Isaac showed us a field of wheat, as tall as ourselves, heavy with grain ripening in the sun. Round the edges of the field, red poppies and smokey-blue foxgloves bloomed. Each flower was visited by an endless procession of flying, buzzing insects – busy brown worker bees, bushy black bumbles, flies with red wings, flies with green wings, all taking and sharing the sweet nectar and golden pollen.

A butterfly landed on Beanpole's arm. 'A red admiral!' It fanned its scarlet wings, drunk on sweetness and sunshine. Other butterflies fluttered past in a kaleidoscope of colours, yellow, white, red, black and brown. The red admiral flapped heavily behind them.

Isaac led us to a meadow where the grass was long and green and damp, mixed with white daisies and yellow buttercups. Under straggling alders and leafy willows a stream bubbled and burbled, patiently wearing boulders to pebbles, pebbles to sand.

'Get down and keep very still,' he whispered.

Swallows were trawling for flies just above the water, dipping and swooping from one end of the stream to the other.

'Wait a bit longer,' said Isaac.

My knees cracked and I was just about to complain, 'Isaac...' when there was a flash of red and bright blue, a soft splash, and then... gone again.

'Kingfisher,' said Isaac.

I breathed again.

'That was wonderful.'

Isaac smiled. 'Winter comes soon enough without wishing the summer away.'

Our summer magic was over and we were back in the cold and draughty shed, but the feeling stayed with us that summer was a magic time to come.

I gave Isaac a hug and said, 'From now on I'll always look forward to summer.'

Alan Brown

Adventures of Tom Sawyer

About midnight Joe awoke, and called the boys. There was a brooding oppressiveness in the air that seemed to bode something. The boys huddled themselves together, and sought the friendly companionship of the fire, though the dull dead heat of the breathless atmosphere was stifling. They sat still, intent and waiting. Beyond the light of the fire, everything was swallowed up in the blackness of darkness. Presently there came a quivering glow that vaguely revealed the foliage for a moment then vanished. By-and-by another came, a little stronger. Then another. Then a faint moan came sighing through the branches of the forest, and the boys felt a fleeting breath upon their cheeks, and shuddered with the fancy that the Spirit of the Night had gone by. There was a pause. Now a weird flash turned night into day, and showed every little grass-blade separate and distinct, that grew about their feet. And it showed three white, startled faces too. A deep peal of thunder went rolling and tumbling down the heavens, and lost itself in sullen rumblings in the distance. A sweep of chilly air passed by, rustling all the leaves and snowing the flaky ashes broadcast about the fire. Another fierce glare lit up the forest, and an instant crash followed that seemed to rend the tree-tops right over the boys' heads. They clung together in terror in the thick gloom that followed. A few big rain-drops fell pattering upon the leaves.

'Quick, boys, go for the tent!' exclaimed Tom.

They sprang away, stumbling over roots and among vines in the dark, no two plunging in the same direction. A furious blast roared through the trees, making everything sing as it went. One blinding flash after another came, and peal on peal of deafening thunder. And now a drenching rain poured down, and the rising hurricane drove it in sheets along the ground. The boys cried out to each other, but the roaring wind and the booming thunder-blasts drowned their voices utterly. However, one by one they struggled in at last, and took shelter under the tent, cold, scared, and streaming with water; but to have company in misery seemed something to be grateful for. They could not talk, the old sail flapped so furiously, even if the other noises would have allowed them. The tempest rose higher and higher, and presently the sail tore loose from its fastenings, and went winging away on the blast. The boys seized each other's hands, and fled, with many tumblings and bruises, to the shelter of a great oak that stood upon the river bank. Now the battle was at its highest. Under the ceaseless conflagration of lightnings that flamed in the skies, everything below stood out in clean-cut and shadowless distinctness; the bending trees, the billowy river white with foam, the driving spray of spume-flakes, the dim outlines of the high bluffs on the other side, glimpsed through the drifting cloud-rack and the slanting veil of rain. Every little while some giant tree yielded the fight and fell crashing through the younger growth; and the unflagging thunder-peals came now in ear-splitting explosive bursts, keen and sharp, and unspeakably appalling. The storm culminated in one matchless effort that seemed likely to tear the island to pieces, burn it up, drown it to the tree-tops, blow it away and deafen every creature in it, all at one and the same moment. It was a wild night for homeless young heads to be out in.

Mark Twain

The Christmas Tree Man

His house is far out. Farther out than you can imagine anyone living. It's small and clean and white. Most summers it's cool; most winters it's warm.

It's a good house for a man alone.

The man himself is a small man, and skinny. He has never married. He has no one. And each year, he grows older.

He didn't know he would live his life alone. When he was a boy, and his name was Garnet Ash, he lived with his family on a street in a town not too big. He was a regular boy. He played football and he fished and he camped out in his backyard. But because he loved being at home most of all, he had few friends and spent most of his days with his parents. Each night he fell asleep listening to their soft voices moving from room to room.

But before Garnet Ash had barely grown up, quite suddenly, his parents died. And Garnet Ash didn't know what to do with himself, with them gone, his family. He hadn't had time to find a wife. And with suddenly no family to whom he could bring a wife, with suddenly no father who could build a nice kitchen table for her, with suddenly no mother who could give summer roses to her... with suddenly no one at all, Garnet Ash didn't know what to do except to go on having no one at all.

He couldn't live in his town any longer. He missed his father and mother too much. So he found a small white house far out, and he moved away, farther out than you could imagine.

And he found an occupation that kept him living, that has kept him living so many, many years.

Garnet Ash is a Christmas Tree Man. Now, few people know him by his real name. They know him only as the Christmas Tree Man.

All round his small white house grow those Christmas trees. Garnet Ash plants them and he raises them like children. Some fat, some lopsided, some strong like rocks and others too weak to try any more.

Like anything else, his trees bring him joy and sorrow.

At certain times of the year, Garnet Ash will drive his old truck out and into the towns to get groceries and fertiliser and paraffin and saplings. But apart from these few trips into the world of grocers and farmers and nursery men, Garnet Ash lives out each of his years alone.

In March, when purple crocuses spurt up through the snow, he stands and admires them alone. In June, when hornets build a nest under the eaves of his house, he stands and worries alone. And in October, when the moon is giant and orange, he stands and whispers to it alone. He often thinks of his parents.

And all this time, his children are growing.

But Garnet Ash, who spends his birthdays alone, who eats Thanksgiving dinner alone, who watches the beginning of each winter and spring and summer and autumn alone – come December, he will be surrounded.

They drive out from the towns in their cars to find him. The cars are shiny and white or red or yellow. In them there is always more than one person and usually there are three or four or five.

They are families. They need a Christmas tree. And they have come looking for the Christmas Tree Man.

Garnet Ash expects them. Every year. And even after all these many years of seeing them drive up to his small, clean white house, he has not grown tired of them.

On the first day of December Garnet Ash is full of anticipation. He trembles with it. He stands before his mirror and trims his hair, combs his beard, plucks his brows a bit. He reaches into the back of a drawer and pulls forth his best red reindeer scarf.

He is looking forward to the company.

The people park their shiny cars and the doors open and out they climb, mothers and fathers and children and grandparents, and they are filled up with life, with hope, with wanting a tree.

The Christmas Tree Man in the red reindeer scarf welcomes them and they say hallo, how are you, getting cold isn't it, do you have a good crop this year?

And Garnet Ash gestures to his fields, he introduces his children, he says, 'I have a good crop.'

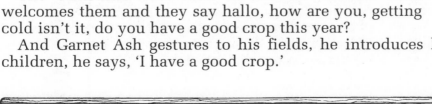

So the men and the women and the children and even sometimes the dogs they have brought with them will hurry into the rows of sleeping green trees, quiet green trees. The snow will crack under their boots and the mist of their breathing will rise up to the sky and they will prowl through the fields of the Christmas Tree Man.

Garnet Ash is happy. He is proud. He says, 'Merry Christmas!' and waves to them as they drive off, their shiny cars sprouting bushy pine tails. Sometimes a boy will lean out of a car window, waving, and the eyes of Garnet Ash will soften and his smile will slacken and he will think he is waving to himself. To himself and his family driving off in that car.

The cars will keep coming, every day, and at night too. Everyone looking for the Christmas Tree Man. And when all of his best trees are gone and there is nothing to offer but a lopsided tree, a skinny tree, a short tree, Garnet Ash will give the people bags of hot chestnuts to ease their disappointment. Eating chestnuts, they'll decide a lopsided tree isn't so bad, really.

Finally, on Christmas Eve, there will be only one or two cars.

Then, Garnet Ash will be alone.

Very late in the night on Christmas Eve, he will walk through his fields, among the stumps of the trees left behind.

'So, not pretty enough for them, eh?' he will say to one of his children. 'Well, lucky for you, I'd say!'

He will walk through the stumps and the trees, and the moon will be large and white and the sky clear and deep, and the rabbits will watch him from the edges of his fields.

Garnet Ash will walk until he finds the weakest tree among those left to stand, the sorriest tree. And he will unwind his red reindeer scarf from round his neck and he will drape it on the top boughs of his ugly child.

Then, very late, Garnet Ash will walk back to his small, clean white house and he will smile to himself and think what it is to be a Christmas Tree Man.

Cynthia Rylant

Earthmaker

Native American cultures inhabit worlds made luminous with stories, spoken or sung. Without a fixed text, each telling demands a creative collaboration between the storyteller, the listener and the tale. To approximate such a chemistry, read the text aloud to yourself several times before putting it aside. Then, after having absorbed its central images, tell the story simply, but place it OUT THERE. Describe what you see unfolding, the story's panorama. At different times you might notice new features – don't be afraid to explore or amplify them. With each retelling the story comes alive in a different way. Use your whole body to give the story some physical substance. Use any repetitions for momentum, a sense of rhythm. Remember, you are the active ingredient in recreating this or any other story. [Please note: the shifting gender of Earthmaker is quite intentional.]

Earthmaker rested.

Out of the darkness and surrounding silence she had created light, then colour. From a pool of her own tears Earthmaker had formed the sun and moon and stars, the plants, and all the creatures who lived in the universe. She had made a time and place for everything.

And yet she felt uneasy, even a little sad as the cold breath of winter approached. She named this time the Moon of Falling Leaves. He understood how the flowers would fade, the grasses tumble down brown, the trees shed their leaves in the lengthening shadows. Their colours would soon be bleached white by the SnowSnake of winter. Earthmaker accepted that this had to be. She herself had made it so.

Hers was a grand plan for those petals which fell from the flowers, those leaves which the trees shed, the tumbling mounds of grasses. They would weave themselves into a warm blanket over the land, a friendly quilt, protecting fragile seeds from any winter chill. Until next spring, until the arrival of the Planting Moon.

And yet it made her heart heavy.

The plants reacted, too. They couldn't understand why they had to crumble and fade away. A Council was summoned which all the trees and flowers and grasses attended. In her lonely silence Earthmaker listened to them discuss their fate.

'Our leaves shelter the winged ones and feed the four-leggeds,' said the Trees to the assembled circle of plants.

'Our colours make everyone's eyes dance,' the Flowers murmured.

'Brothers and Sisters, we are Earthmaker's hair. How could she cut us off without reason?' shouted the Grasses. 'Why can't we stay with her? It doesn't seem right.' They all nodded in agreement.

Earthmaker listened closely to their words. She considered for quite a long time how they were feeling. Suddenly a different vision swept through him like a windstorm of falling leaves. 'With the grasses gone, with the leaves vanished, with the bare bones of trees wrapped in snow, what colours will the children be able to see? They might lose hope. They might forget. 'Quiet now, Earthmaker's breathing slowed down to an almost imperceptible movement, like the flow of seasons which she had tried so hard to protect.

Changes must be made. She had power. She was after all Earthmaker, and her thinking made it so.

Earthmaker revealed to the plants gathered in Council her reason for making them give way to winter. In return for protecting the future, she allowed the leaves one last flush of colour, reds and golds and ochres, as a silent farewell. To this day Indian Summer marks the approach of winter. It's named after Indian people because they were the only ones considerate enough to believe her winter-telling stories.

Earthmaker allowed some plants, like the juniper, to keep their green leaves all year long, to remind us that colour would eventually return. Even so their shiny leaves remain hard, as if frozen by an invisible winter.

To the flowers she gave a special silhouette. So they should not be forgotten, Earthmaker splashed their finely ground colours across the sky after each renewing rainfall. That's how rainbows came into the world, to commemorate the passing of flowers.

Then Earthmaker remembered her children.

'I must give them something of their own size to appreciate. Colours must never disappear from their hearts. They must be kept alive with wonder.'

Then she wandered at random, collecting a strip of silver birch here, purple flowers from the sacred tobacco there, the hard blue sassafras nut, some flaming yellow jessamine, saltbush, teaberry, checkerberry, partridgeberry, boxberry, spiceberry, wild sunflowers.

As soon as her storybag was full Earthmaker mustered all the children she could find around his winter-telling fire. To their rapt ears she revealed why leaves fall to earth, how rainbows came into being, and when Indian Summer began. Opening her storybag Earthmaker said, 'Here children, these colours are for you.' All at once thousand of dazzling butterflies stormed from his bag, a flurry of Indian Summer leaves. Like bright spirits they released every hue, tint, tone and shade imaginable. But there was more than delight in the children's eyes, there were songs as well which seemed to come directly from the butterflies' wings. Songs of colours.

But a chorus of plant voices scolded Earthmaker, saying: 'You gave us colours to delight in, but no voices to sing about them. We have no music to get people's attention, just our own silent colours. It's not fair! It's not right. Not after the sacrifices we've made, giving up our lives for the world.'

Earthmaker realised the plants were right. Their pride had to be respected so she took back her songs given to the butterflies. Ever since that time, the butterflies have been silent like the flowers who can only display their songs through colour.

Unless you listen hard enough that is, or so they say.

Retold from Sioux and Papago legends by Richard Cupidi

LIVING THINGS

I would never choose a dragon for a pet

Someday I will look at all of the animals. I will pick out the one I like best. I will take it home and keep it for a pet.

I might buy a fish in a shiny bowl. I would put it in my room and watch it swim around and around all day.

BUT I WOULD NEVER CHOOSE A DRAGON FOR A PET!

It would be hard to find a place to keep a dragon. If I kept him in the garage, what would Dad say when he tried to put the car in there? If I kept him under the bed, what would Mum say when she tried to sweep in there?

I think I would rather have a kitten. A kitten would drink milk from a little dish in the kitchen. She would lick her paws and wash her face. It would be fun to feed a kitten.

BUT FEED A DRAGON? NEVER!

Even if I made him wash his claws before he came to dinner, he would probably eat from the serving dish or lean his elbows on the table. He would eat too fast and get the hiccups. A dragon with the hiccups is very, very loud.

I might buy a rabbit. I could let him hop around the garden and nibble the green grass. Sometimes I would take him for a walk in town.

BUT TAKE A DRAGON FOR A WALK? NEVER!

If he wagged his tail a little bit, he might knock down a telephone pole. If he sneezed, he could easily blow down sixteen buildings.

Instead, I might choose a puppy. A puppy is warm and wriggly. We would play hide-and-seek or wrestle on the living room floor.

BUT HOW COULD YOU WRESTLE A DRAGON?

I think it would be better if I chose a bird. She could sit on my shoulder or finger and I would teach her to sing.

BUT TEACH A DRAGON TO SING? IMPOSSIBLE!

He would make horrible, terrifying, petrifying noises that would cause my knees to tremble and shake.

No, I should be smart and choose a pony. He would have big, brown eyes and a long mane and tail. He would take me for rides all around the yard.

BUT RIDE A DRAGON?

What a scary thing to do! I would be as tall as the houses and as high as the sky. If he started to trot, I'd probably cry.

I'll get a duck. He could swim in my pool and quack and quack.

But dragons hate water. Wet feet make them roar. No! A dragon won't do!

Someday I will look at all the animals. I might choose a fish or a kitten, or a rabbit, or a puppy, or a bird, or a pony or a duck.

BUT I WOULD NEVER CHOOSE A DRAGON FOR A PET!

Would you?

Betty Lacey

===

When I lived down Cuckoo Lane... and came by tadpoles

My best friend's father was making a pond. He put in rushes, waterlilies and goldfish. The next day the goldfish had gone.

Fred, my best friend's cat, lay on the grass. He warmed his furry orange tum in the warm spring sunshine. He purred... and sometimes he burped.

More goldfish were put in the pond. And went.

Next a net was placed over the water. But what was the good of a pond you couldn't peer into? Dip in your fingers and flick water about? So the net went too. And so did the next lot of goldfish.

'Yer pays yer money, and yer takes yer choice,' said my best friend's father. Which sounded very strange, since he was a teacher.

My best friend put her arms round Fred, who scratched all down the side of her face. But what were a few pretty fish compared with a furry, purry, scratchy cat?

Then my best friend's grandmother, knitting in a deckchair, said, 'Tadpoles.'

'Aha!' My best friend's father pointed at Fred. 'Some jumping frogs might teach you a lesson, my lad.'

'Frogs aren't tadpoles,' my best friend said.

'To start with they are. They grow into frogs later. Now, where can we come by some tadpoles?'

The next day, Sunday, I woke up early. Outside in the road somebody was whistling. I ran to the window. Where was Pat going so early? And why was he carrying a jam jar on a string?

Later on, after breakfast, I went down Cuckoo Lane to call for my best friend. Behind the gardens on that side of the road was rough wild land called the jungle. On the edge of the jungle, by a slimy ditch, tall trees grew. From the tree behind my best friend's house hung a rope with a knot on the end. We took turns to sit on the knot, and swing. And sooner or later one of us would say, 'Now let's play Ghost Rides.' It was our own special game. The swinger closed her eyes, while the other one pushed and did ghostly things. Flapped floppy leaves in her face. Brushed her arms and legs with grasses. Made terrible blood-curdling wails. Or horrible ghostly groans. And the swinger never opened her eyes, whatever.

That Sunday the scary bit never got going. I swung and swung and swung.
'Go on, push!'
Nothing happened.
'*Do something*. If you don't I'll open my eyes.'
Still nothing.
I was just about to open them when... WHOOMPH! Off I went again!
'Not so hard,' I shouted, but....
WHOOMPH! Whoomph!! *Whoomph!!!*
I was swinging higher than ever before. Had my best friend gone bananas?
Then on my next swing backwards I heard a whistle. Opening my eyes I saw two jam jars down at the base of the tree.
'Ow!' yelled a solid lump of boy as I dropped off on top of him.
'Where's my best friend?' I asked, after we'd sorted ourselves out.
'Captured.' Pat ran down into the slimy ditch, then up the other side. 'And you're dead,' he said when I followed him.
'I'm not.'
'You are. You didn't watch out, and just fell into a big swollen river.'
'I didn't, I didn't.'
'You did, you did. You've been swept away. You're not here at all.'
'You fell in too!'
'I'm a champion swimmer, so I'm all right.'
My best friend was in her garden tied to the clothes pole. There was a pillowcase over her head, and Mick was doing a war dance.
Fred came prowling down the path.
'There's a big wild beast,' Mick prodded the pillowcase, 'coming to finish you off.'
An angry buzz came out of the pillowcase.
I ran and untied my best friend. Under the pillowcase she had a white thing tied round her mouth. Her grandmother's summer vest!

Mick and Pat vanished into the jungle. But after we'd pegged the pillowcase and vest back on the line, we found they'd forgotten the jam jars. Inside was water, and little dark brown darting things. We took them to my best friend's father.
'Just the job. Tadpoles.'
'How can they be tadpoles?' my best friend asked. 'They're not a bit like frogs.'
'Not yet. But just you watch.' He

emptied the jam jars into the pond. Fred came to watch, but the tadpoles were too quick for him.

After we'd put the empty jam jars back under the tree we hurried back to the pond. We watched all day. The tadpoles stayed the same, but by the end of the day the jam jars had gone.

On Monday Pat and Mick caught us in the playground. 'Murderers!' said Mick.

'Tadpole killers!' said Pat.

'We're not. We're not.'

'Where are they then?' Mick pulled my arms behind my back. 'Did you feed them to that orange beast?'

'We didn't. We didn't.'

'If you really want to know,' my best friend said in a haughty voice, 'the tadpoles are living in our pond. Turning into frogs.'

Next Sunday Pat and Mick came to see for themselves. The tadpoles had grown bigger. Some even had little legs. Pat and Mick were so pleased they asked us to go with them over the swamps to get some more.

We wanted to go, but we weren't allowed. Perhaps it was just as well. Mick sank, and lost one of his gum boots. Pat dropped his jam jar coming home, and all his tadpoles went down the drain.

Mick put his in my best friend's pond with the others. They all grew into lovely little hopping frogs. And for all I know their ancestors are there to this very day.

Jean Willis

Things are puzzling

A little girl was walking along a footpath through a field, when she happened to meet an elephant.

'What is your name?' asked the elephant.

'Cristina,' said the little girl.

'You are very small,' said the elephant.

'Yes, I am a small little girl.'

'Goodbye,' said the elephant.

The next thing Cristina happened to meet was a mouse.

'What are you?' asked the mouse.

'I am a small little girl,' said Cristina.

'You are very big,' said the mouse.

'Goodbye,' said Cristina, as she walked on.

The next thing she happened to meet was a giraffe.

'Hallo,' said the giraffe. 'What are you?'

'I am a big small little girl,' said Cristina.

'You are very short,' said the giraffe, bending his neck down so as to look at her closer.

Cristina said goodbye and walked on. The next thing she happened to meet on the smooth footpath was a very round and prickly hedgehog.

He stopped and looked up at Cristina.

'What are you?' he asked.

'I am a short big small little girl.'

'You are very tall,' said the

hedgehog decidedly and trotted off before Cristina could say goodbye.

The next animal she happened to meet was a snake. She was not at all frightened, because she had never seen a snake before. But it ought to be mentioned that it is wise to be frightened of snakes until you have been introduced.

'What are you?' asked the snake.

'I am a tall short big small little girl,' answered Cristina.

'You are very fat,' said the snake.

'Goodbye,' said Cristina, as the snake rippled off amongst the grass.

The next animal she happened to meet was a pig – a huge overgrown pig, grunting loudly.

'What are you?' he asked.

'I am a fat tall short big small little girl.'

'You are *very* thin,' said the pig, grunting.

'Goodbye,' said Cristina.

The next animal she saw was a bird. It skimmed out of the sky and perched on a branch over the footpath.

'What are you?' asked the bird.

'I am a thin fat tall short big small little girl,' answered Cristina, who was beginning to get tired of being so many different things.

'Well, you are very slow,' said the bird, chirping. 'While you have been walking across this small field, I have flown three times round the world.'

But he was lying. He had only been round it once.

'Goodbye,' said Cristina, leaving the bird to rest on the branch.

The next animal she happened to meet was a tortoise.

'What are you?' asked the tortoise, rather out of breath from trying to hurry.

'I am a slow thin fat tall short big small little girl. *And* I know what you're going to say next. You are going to say that I am very quick.'

'I wasn't,' said the tortoise decidedly in his dry, scratchy voice. 'I forget *what* I was going to say. You have put it out of my head.'

'Well, perhaps you can tell me,' Cristina went on, 'why it is that I am called so many different things.'

'Things are very puzzling,' answered the tortoise. 'It depends how you *feel*, not what people say.

Take me, for instance. They call me slow, but I often feel quite quick. When I go for a walk with my grandfather, who is a hundred and seventy-three years old, he says I am far too quick for him. Goodbye for now.'

Cristina decided to go home and have tea. That at least was not puzzling.

James Reeves

Marna's paper bag

One afternoon, on her way home from school, Marna threw away a paper bag. She ran home and forgot all about it, but next morning, when she walked by the spot again, the bag was still there on the ground, and there was a tin can lying next to it. She didn't worry about it, because she thought that somebody would come along and clear it away.

While she was at school a man passed by the spot. He had a sweet packet in his hand. He looked around for a rubbish bin, but when he couldn't see one, he threw down the sweet packet beside the can and the paper bag. 'The street cleaner will sweep it up,' he said to himself, and went on his way.

During the course of the day two ladies got off the bus at the corner of the street. As they walked passed the spot where the little heap of rubbish was lying, they threw down their bus tickets and continued along the street without giving them another thought. And so it went on. When Marna came out of school that afternoon, there was quite a large heap of litter lying where she had thrown down the paper bag. She wondered for a moment why the man who swept the street hadn't been along that day, but she had other things to do, so off she ran without thinking any more about it.

It so happened that the man who swept the streets was ill, and no replacement could be found for him, so the street remained unswept for several days. Everyone who passed the spot deposited something, thinking that it must be the place where the street-sweeper had brushed the litter into one neat pile.

At the end of the week a man who was tidying his garden began to look for a place to throw down his garden waste. 'It's much too far to take it to the dump,' he said to his wife.

'Then why don't you take it down the street,' she responded. 'There's a place down there where everybody seems to be leaving their rubbish. I daresay the man will be along soon to collect it.'

So the gardening man wheeled his wheelbarrow down the street and deposited his rubbish on the heap. Then he went back to his nice tidy garden, quite pleased with himself. His neighbour had seen what had happened. 'That would be a good place to take all the building rubble I have lying around my house,' he said. 'I'll borrow the wheelbarrow and take it now.' He had to make several trips to the heap, but his house was soon looking so neat and tidy that he didn't mind that.

All the people in the street began to notice what was happening. They could not resist the temptation to dump all their rubbish on the convenient heap, and at the end of the month there were old mattresses, buckets with holes in them, piles of old clothes, chairs with the stuffing sticking out of them, and lots more. Somebody pushed along an old motor car and left it there, blocking the street and causing a traffic jam. Nobody could walk along the street now, and Marna couldn't get to school.

'Why doesn't somebody come along and clear up the rubbish?' the people began to say to each other. 'It's quite disgraceful leaving it there. It's beginning to smell.'

And so it was. The people who lived in that street had to keep all their doors and windows tightly shut, and when they went out to catch the bus at the end of the street, they had to pinch their noses between their fingers and thumbs.

One day it started to rain. All day the rain poured down out of a heavy black sky. The heap of rubbish was lying on top of the drain, so the water could not run away. The houses were flooded. The shops were flooded. The school was flooded. 'Will somebody go and complain to the authorities!' screamed the people. 'Get the police and the fire brigade! Do something!'

Marna watched, and listened, but said nothing. She thought about her paper bag. She knew that it was her paper bag that had started it all.

The street-sweeper heard what had happened, and he sent a message to the people who lived in the street: 'Every one of you must take away the rubbish that you left there.'

At first the people were offended. 'We'll do no such thing!' they cried. 'Other people left their rubbish there, too. Why shouldn't we?' But as the rain got heavier and the water crept higher, they knew they had to do something. They waded through the water and began to take away their own rubbish. Soon the drain was cleared. The water began to flow away. The rain stopped, and the sun came out. Marna ran out of her house. Only a few scraps of soggy paper were left in the street, but Marna knew they were all that remained of her paper bag. She picked them up as best she could. 'I'll never throw anything down in the street again,' she said to herself. And she never did; nor did any of the people who lived in that street, and anyone will tell you that Marna's street, to this very day, is the cleanest one you could ever wish to find.

Linda Allen

Old Station

Most dogs have one name, but Pooch had three – one after the other. Pooch was what Grandma called him in the first place. But when Nick was a toddler he couldn't say Pooch very well and so Pooch soon became Pooh.

Then one day Pooh heard the rattle of the milk bottles outside and came bounding out of the house to say hallo to the milkman – he liked the milkman. But today it was a different one. Pooh prowled around him sniffing at the bottom of his trousers. The new milkman went as white as his milk. Nick tried to drag Pooh back into the house, but he wouldn't come.

'S'like a wolf,' said the milkman, putting his hands on his head and backing down the path. 'You ought to chain it up.'

'Not a wolf,' Nick said. 'He's an old station.'

'A what?' said the milkman.

'An old station,' Nick said. 'Pooh is an old station.' At that moment Grandma came to the door.

'Nick gets his words muddled sometimes,' she said. 'He's only little. I think he means an *Alsation*, don't you dear? Old Station! You are a funny boy, Nick.' And she laughed so much that she nearly cried. So from that day Pooh was called Old Station.

There were always just the three of them in the house. Nick had lived with Grandma for as long as he could remember. She looked after Nick and Old Station looked after them both. Everywhere they went Old Station went with them. 'Don't know what we'd do without him,' Grandma would say.

All his life Old Station had been like a big brother to Nick. Nick was nine years old now. He had watched Old Station grow old as he grew up. The old dog moved slowly these days, and when he got up in the morning to go outside you could see it was a real effort. He would spend most of the day asleep in his basket, dreaming his dreams.

Nick watched him that morning as he ate his cornflakes before he went off to school. It was the last day before half-term. Old Station was growling in his sleep as he often did and his whiskers were twitching.

'He's chasing cats in his dreams,' said Grandma. 'Hurry up, Nick, else you'll be late.' She gave him his satchel and packed lunch, and Nick called out 'Goodbye' to Old Station and ran off down the road.

It was a windy autumn morning with the leaves falling all around him. Before he got to school he caught twenty-six of them in mid-air and that was more than he'd ever caught before. By the end of the day the leaves were piled as high as his ankles in the gutters, and Nick scuffled through them on the way back home, thinking of all the bike rides he could go on now that half-term had begun.

Old Station wasn't there to meet him at the door as he sometimes was, and Grandma wasn't in the kitchen cooking tea as she usually was. Old Station wasn't in his basket either.

Nick found Grandma in the back garden, taking the washing off the line. 'Nice windy day. Wanted to leave the washing out as long as possible,' she said from behind a sheet. 'I'll get your tea in a minute, dear.'

'Where's Old Station?' Nick said. 'He's not in his basket.'

Grandma didn't reply, not at first anyway; and when she did Nick wished she never had done.

'He had to go,' Grandma said simply, and she walked past him without even looking at him.

'Go where?' Nick asked. 'What do you mean? Where's he gone to?'

Grandma put the washing down on the kitchen table and sat down heavily in the chair. Nick could see then that she'd been crying, and he knew that Old Station was dead. 'The vet said he was suffering,' she said, looking up at him. 'We couldn't have him suffering, could we? It had to be done. That's all there is to it. Just a pinprick it was, dear, and then he went off to sleep. Nice and peaceful.'

'He's dead then,' Nick said.

Grandma nodded. 'I buried him outside in the garden by the wall. It's what was best for him Nick,' she said. 'You know that don't you?' Nick nodded and they cried quietly together.

Michael Morpurgo

Eight hairy legs

There was a spider in the bath. Jeremy James was sitting on the lavatory, and he just happened to look sideways and downwards, and there was the spider. It wasn't one of those tiny, tickly ones – he didn't mind those. No, it was one of those large leg-spreading ones, black and hairy and shuddery – the sort that make your backbone run up and down your body.

It's not easy to think about other things when there's a black spider sprawling less than three feet away from your bare legs. At any moment it could come scrabbling up the bath and on to your foot, legs, tummy... ugh! Besides, where there's one spider there could be other spiders, and there's just no telling where they might crawl to. Jeremy James immediately felt a goose-pimply tingle at the back of his neck, and slapped it hard to make sure the goose-pimple didn't creep down on to his back. Then the thought occurred to him that if a spider got into the bath, another spider might get into the lavatory, and then just think where that could creep to! He leapt off the seat and looked into the pan. Nothing.

He looked down into the bath again, just in time to see the spider take a quick scuttly step towards the plughole. Then it stopped still again, legs slightly bent, as if tensed to do a mighty leap. If it leapt out of the bath, Jeremy James decided he would leap out of the bathroom. But what should he do if it stayed in the bath?

Jeremy James remembered a spider that had once been hanging on his bedroom wall. He had known then that he'd never be able to sleep while it was there, and so he'd taken his bedroom slipper and given the spider a whack. But the result had been a horrible mess. Half the spider had been squelched into the wall, and the other half had been squelched into the slipper, and Mummy had had to come and wipe all the bits and pieces away with a wet cloth. Even then, Jeremy James hadn't slept very well, because he kept imagining spider-legs running all over him.

On another occasion he'd called for Daddy, and Daddy had arrived with a large sheet of newspaper.

'Let's have a look then,' Daddy had said, and with the newspaper spread wide he had advanced on the spider and had suddenly jammed the paper against the wall and at great speed screwed it up into a big ball.

'He won't trouble you any more,' Daddy had said. 'He's either dead or studying the sports news.'

But Jeremy James had seen something Daddy had not seen, and he asked Daddy to unscrew the paper again. And when Daddy unscrewed the paper, he found to his surprise that there was nothing there except for sports news. Then they had spent half an hour trying in vain to attract a spider that clearly wasn't interested in sport. That had been another sleepless night.

Well, at least this was morning, and the spider was in the bathroom, not the bedroom. But the problem was the same – how do you get rid of a spider without making it into a mess or a magic vanishing act?

The spider twitched and twiddled itself one step nearer the plughole. Jeremy James had an idea. Another few steps and it would be near enough for him to turn the tap on and swoosh it away down the hole. No mess at all. In fact, as clean an end as you could wish for.

'Move!' said Jeremy James. 'Go on! Shoo! Quick march!'

The spider did not even slow-march. Jeremy James stood and looked at the spider, and the spider stood and looked at Jeremy James. This was not going to be easy. Jeremy James needed a weapon, and his eye fell on the bathbrush. A scratch with those bristles should make even the toughest spider jump. It might even take the brush for a monster with a moustache and die of fright.

Jeremy James ran the bathbrush along the bottom of the bath, until the bristles were almost touching what might be the spider's eighth little toenail. The spider remained very still. Jeremy James moved the brush again so that it just touched the tip of the spidery toe. The spider twitched.

Probably thought it had an itch. Jeremy James pushed the brush firmly against the spider's leg. With a scurry and a flurry the spider raced forward, while Jeremy James leapt back and dropped the brush in the bath with a clatter.

Now his heart was jumping like a grasshopper with hiccups. This was turning out to be a dangerous battle. In the past he'd killed snakes and crocodiles and man-eating tigers in the bath, but none of them had given him half as much trouble as this spider. There it lurked, hairy legs spread wide apart, waiting to pounce and cover him with shivers. Two inches away from the plughole.

Gradually Jeremy James's heart sat down again in his chest. If he could just push the spider with the brush and then whoosh it with the tap, he could send it sailing down the Seven Seas. On the other hand, it might grab hold of the brush and come racing over the bristles, handle, hand, arm....

Heroes don't think about might-be's. Jeremy James leaned over the bath, picked up the brush, and with eyes swivelling like tennis-watchers he reached for the tap nearest the spider.

Swoosh and sweep! Down came the water and the brush, and as the spider struggled to swim up the bath, so Jeremy James pushed it down again. But the flow of water kept bringing the spider back up the bath again. Jeremy James turned the tap off, and the water sucked the spider back towards the hole.

'Down you go!' said Jeremy James.

And with eight despairing waves and a loud gurgle, the spider disappeared from view.

Bathbrush in hand, Jeremy James stood triumphant.

'Jeremy James!' came Mummy's voice from the landing. 'Haven't you finished in there?'

'I've just been killing a spider,' said Jeremy James.

'Well hurry up. I'm waiting to bath the twins!' called Mummy.

'It was a huge spider!' said Jeremy James. 'And it nearly killed *me*!'

But Mummy didn't seem interested. Perhaps she might have been more interested if the spider *had* killed Jeremy James. Then she might have wished she'd thought more about spiders and less about baths and twins.

Jeremy James sat down on the lavatory again, legs dangling and lips pouting. What was the use of being a hero if nobody was interested? He glanced sadly down at the scene of his heroism – and his glance got stuck into a long and disbelieving stare: there, on the edge of the plughole, looking a little damp and dazed and drippy, was the ghost of the drowned spider.

Jeremy James leapt off the lavatory as if it had been a pin-cushion. 'Mummy!' he cried.

'What is it?' asked Mummy from one of the bedrooms.

'There's a spider in the bath!' cried Jeremy James.

'I thought you'd killed it,' said Mummy, now on the landing.

Jeremy James unlocked the bathroom door, and Mummy came in.

'Ugh!' she said. 'What a monster!'

'I did kill it,' said Jeremy James, 'but it must have unkilled itself.'

'Well, this is what we do with spiders,' said Mummy. On the bathroom shelf, next to the toothbrush stand, was the mouthwash glass, which Mummy picked up in her right hand. With her left, she tore off a sheet of toilet paper. 'Now watch carefully,' she said.

Then she bent over the bath, and put the glass upside down round the spider. She slid the sheet of paper under the glass and under the spider, turned the glass the right way up, and plop! There was the spider sitting at the bottom of the glass.

'He doesn't look quite so big now, does he?' said Mummy, holding the glass so that Jeremy James could see.

In fact the spider seemed quite small and silly, sitting there looking out at Jeremy James looking in.

'What shall we do with him?' asked Mummy.

'Can we throw him out of the window?' suggested Jeremy James.

'Good idea,' said Mummy.

She opened the window, leaned out, and with a flick of her wrist sent the spider diving down to the lawn below. Then she showed Jeremy James the empty glass, which she washed out and replaced on the bathroom shelf.

'And now,' said Mummy, 'perhaps you'll do what you're supposed to be doing.'

Mummy left the bathroom, and Jeremy James perched on the lavatory again. It was amazing how simple things were when Mummy did them. He looked all round the bathroom, hoping to see another spider so that he could do the trick with the glass and paper. But there wasn't a spider to be seen.

There was just one thing about Mummy's trick that slightly worried Jeremy James. It was nothing very important, but when a little later he cleaned his teeth, he rinsed his mouth with water straight from the tap. He didn't really need a glass for that anyway.

David Henry Wilson

Pollution!

People in Bestburg were proud of their town and especially of their park. David and Sara lived near the park. On sunny afternoons they often went to play there after school.

Their favourite spot was near the pond. Water lilies grew in it. Catkins and rushes could be found around the edges. David and Sara liked to watch the animal life in and around the pond. Insects flew over the pond, and some skated on top of the water. Fish and frogs lived there and ate the insects that hovered over the water or fell into it.

In spring the pond was full of new life. There were squiggly tadpoles that would grow into frogs. Baby ducklings followed the mother duck.

The buds on the big old oak tree near the pond opened into leaves and made a fine shady place. One day the children saw a squirrel scurrying up the oak tree. 'What does she have in her mouth?' Sara asked.

'She is carrying food to her babies up in that hole,' David said.

When the children looked closely at the trees and bushes, they saw caterpillars and other insects. They watched birds eating the insects on the bark and leaves, and decided that the trees were the birds' supermarket as well as their home.

One year a factory was built on the outskirts of the town. There weren't enough people in Bestburg to do all the jobs in the factory, so new people moved to the town. Houses and blocks of flats were built so that they had a place to live.

When the factory began to work, a dark cloud of smoke billowed from the chimneys, and hung over the town and the park. The town was more crowded and the people were busier. There was more rubbish to get rid of. People became careless about their litter and the park became cluttered with old newspapers and cans. The pond, too, became a dumping place for tyres, oil cans, bottles and paper. Soon the water was dirty and smelly.

The water lilies and rushes could not grow in the dirty, oil-ladened water. With the bad water and no plants to hide among, the frogs and fish either moved to a better pond or died. David and Sara did not go to the park anymore.

The blanket of factory smoke often kept the sun from shining on the town and the park. It made the air bad for the trees. The leaves developed black spots and then fell off. This left no food for the caterpillars and other insects. There was no shelter and food for the birds who flew away to other places. Many of the trees died.

Some of the people in Bestburg began to worry about what had happened to the park and the town. Little by little everyone worked to make Bestburg more the way it had been.

The factory owners agreed to fix the chimneys so that the dark, poisonous smoke would no longer blow over the town. Many people worked together to restore the park. Topsoil was replaced. Trees were planted and the pond was cleaned. Things that people could do happened quickly. Things that had

to wait for nature to repair took longer.

When the pond water was clear, plants began to grow again. Then baby fish could be put in. Insects found their way to the park and the pond. Birds and squirrels followed. Frogs returned to the pond.

Many years later when they were grown up, David and Sara came back to visit Bestburg. The park was full of life again, the pride of Bestburg.

Helen Paladino

Badger's olympical games

The first event was running. There were five animals taking part: Hare, Squirrel, Rabbit, Rat – and, of course, Tortoise.

Hare, who was the favourite, had his ears tied down with a headband.

'Lessens the wind resistance, chaps,' he announced on the starting line. 'Lets me run all the faster.'

Tortoise wasn't put off by this in the slightest. For he had something special, too. On his vest, he had stitched in big, bold letters – SUPERFAST! Just to give himself confidence. He puffed himself up a little, and felt very good indeed!

Badger – not surprisingly – was the official starter. The stadium fell silent as he raised a white flag.

'Three times round the running track,' he declared. 'On your marks... get set....'

Down came the flag.

Tortoise began to move and, to his surprise, he found his legs were going rather well.

'Must have been all that training,' he thought to himself.

He looked up. There was no sign of the others.

'I-I'm even in the lead!' The thought made him smile a little smile.

Poor old Tortoise! He didn't realise that the others were already round the first bend and out of sight.

The crowd cheered and cheered and cheered and Tortoise thought it was all for him.

'If I can just keep going,' he panted, 'I'll win a medal!'

And with that, he put his head down and concentrated on plodding on as fast as he could plod.

From that moment, Tortoise looked at nothing but his feet. He didn't see the others as they sped by him once... and then again.

The stadium was going wild. Every single animal was on its feet, yelling and waving and clapping.

Tortoise allowed himself a quick glance up. His heart almost burst with joy as he saw, stretched across the track before him the winning tape!

With every last ounce of energy, he forced his poor old legs to move faster. The tape got nearer and nearer, and Tortoise got more and more excited!

Then suddenly, his vest – with SUPERFAST! written proudly on it – touched the white tape and broke it!

Tortoise raised his arms into the air. Hare crossed the line just behind him, followed closely by the others.

'Jolly bad luck, Hare,' gasped Tortoise, whose face had a purple tinge to it. 'I was just that bit too fast for you, eh?'

'What do you mean, old chap?' smiled Hare, who was scarcely out of puff. 'I won. We've all been round three times already – you've only gone round once!'

Tortoise swallowed hard, and his heart lurched inside him.

So he hadn't won a medal after all.

'Still, not to worry, old chap,' grinned Hare, who was really very sporting. 'You might do better in the jumping – it's on next.'

Tortoise forced a smile to his lips and plodded over to the jumping pit.

He had a plan. The way Tortoise saw it, he had only one chance of winning the high jump event – and that was to wait until near the end of the competition when the bar was at its highest. He knew he hadn't the energy to do lots and lots of jumps like the others. Tortoise felt he had only one good jump in him, and if he kept it till the very end then perhaps he could surprise them all!

With a warm feeling of excitement inside him Tortoise sat down at the side of the high jump pit – waiting his moment.

It was obvious from the very start who the favourite was.

Frog!

With remarkable ease and agility, he sprang over the bar, quickly eliminating Mouse, Squirrel and Rabbit – who, although they tried very hard, were not nearly good enough.

'Higher! Higher!' cried the crowd, all of whom wanted to see just how high Frog could jump.

Badger, who was the official judge of the event, raised the bar one notch higher.

Frog yawned a little yawn, and hopped cleanly over the bar. It was just too easy for him!

'Higher! Higher!' chanted the crowd, and Badger moved the bar up again.

Once more Frog sprang forward.

Up and over he went!

Again the crowd cheered, and again the bar was put up.

And again. And again. And again.

And all the while, Tortoise watched.

And so it went on, until the bar was too high even for Frog.

This was the moment Tortoise had been waiting for.

The crowd was applauding Frog for all his efforts, and Badger was about to declare him the winner, when Tortoise stepped forward.

'Em... put the bar up again, please,' he said rather casually to Badger. 'I... I think I'd like a go.'

There was silence.

The whole stadium was astonished. They had all forgotten about Tortoise. Surely he couldn't jump higher than Frog?

There was something rather splendid in the confident way he stood there, arms folded, waiting for Badger to place the bar in position.

It was at precisely this moment that Tortoise realised just how high the bar was.

He walked forward and looked up. And up.... And up.... And up.

It was way above his head! This

was going to be his greatest triumph. If he could clear the bar, he'd win a medal and be the hero of Badger's Olympical Games!

Tortoise walked back twelve paces, then stood there, concentrating.

'Oh no, he's gone to sleep!' giggled Hedgehog.

'Quiet, there!' scolded Badger.

Tortoise began to rock to and fro on his feet for a few seconds, then launched himself forward.

The only sound that could be heard in the stadium was the plod, plod, plod noise of his feet as he went faster and faster, until he was going as fast as he could go!

When he was right in front of the bar, Tortoise closed his eyes and jumped with all his might!

He sailed through the air, and flopped down into the warm, soft sand of the jumping pit!

He looked up. The bar was still there! He'd cleared it! He'd soared right over it!

Tortoise stood up and raised his arms aloft to the cheering crowds!

It was only after a couple of minutes that he realised something terrible. They weren't cheering. They were laughing! The entire stadium was in fits of laughter!

Badger came over.

'Bad luck, Tortoise,' he said, trying hard not to laugh himself. 'I'm afraid you didn't quite clear the bar – you shot right underneath the thing!'

And with that, Badger clutched his sides, threw his head back, and simply roared with laughter!

It was rather rude of them all to make fun of poor old Tortoise like that, but it had been a very funny sight!

It was no joke for Tortoise. For the second time that day, he felt a sense of failure seep through him. He sank down into the sand and sat there for a long, long time.

Tortoise would have sat in the jumping pit for ever if it hadn't been for Badger announcing that the next event was throwing the stone, and would all those who had entered this competition make their way to the specially fenced-off area 'without further pausifications'.

Tortoise stood up and brushed the sand from the seat of his shorts.

Although he was very down-hearted when he set off, by the time he arrived he had cheered up quite a bit.

After all, he had as good a chance as anybody else!

It seemed easy enough. All the competitors had to do was to pick up a stone, stand at the line, and throw it. Whoever threw it the farthest won the medal.

Squirrel looked easily the best. It wasn't really surprising; every autumn he spent hours on end throwing big bags of nuts up into a hole in his tree to keep him in food for the winter.

He picked up the stone, tucked it under his chin, spun round once and launched it into the air with a magnificent push.

It was as if the stone had wings. It flew through the air and landed well beyond the little flags which showed how far the others had thrown.

There was only one competitor to go after Squirrel. And that was Tortoise.

This, he decided, was his chance. He'd show them all. He'd give them something to cheer this time.

The stadium was quiet. Every eye was on Tortoise as he walked slowly over to the line.

He bent down to pick up the stone. It was heavier than he thought, but this made him all the more determined to win.

Tortoise tucked the stone under

his chin, the way he'd seen Squirrel do it.

Then he spun round once.

Then twice.

Then three times... then four times....

By the time he'd spun round eleven times, Tortoise realised to his horror that he couldn't stop! And at exactly the same moment it dawned on the crowd that something peculiar was happening.

One by one, they began to smile... then giggle... then chortle... then chuckle... and then howl with laughter at the sight of Tortoise spinning round and round in the centre of the stadium.

Round and round he went, and louder and louder grew the laughter.

Then, suddenly, the stone shot from his hand, flew straight up in the air, and landed with a terrible thud – right on his toes!

Tortoise stopped spinning immediately, and fell in a heap on the ground.

All the animals in the stadium were crying with laughter. All the animals but poor old Tortoise!

He had tears in his eyes all right. But they weren't tears of laughter.

With his foot throbbing, and his head spinning, Tortoise limped and staggered his way out of the stadium.

When he was quite sure that he was alone and that no one could see him, he crawled into some long grass and cried.

A thousand teardrops later, Tortoise stopped sobbing. He heard voices. It was Badger, and lots of other animals. Tortoise poked his head through a clump of ferns. Lined up in a long row in front of his very eyes were mice, and rabbits, and rats, and moles, and squirrels, and hares. There must have been a score or more. They were all wearing skis.

It took Tortoise a minute or so to realise that he'd hobbled right up the slope to the starting point of the ski-ing down the muddy hill event.

Again Badger was the official starter.

'Remember,' he shouted through a megaphone, 'you go right down the slope, keeping between the flags as you descendify. First across the line in the centre of the stadium is the winner.'

He raised the starting pistol.

'On your marks....'

Tortoise leaned forward a little to watch.

'Get set....'

Tortoise leaned forward a little more.

BANG!!! went Badger's starting gun.

Tortoise almost jumped right out of his shell! He felt his feet slither and slip on the damp grass, and before he knew what was happening, he tumbled out of his hidey-hole and landed upside-down on the starting line!

In an instant, he began to slide down the hill after the skiers!

You should have seen him, waving his arms and his legs in the air as he gathered speed.

Bumpity-bump! Thumpity-thump! Clumpity-clump! Down he went, bouncing and bobbing, sliding and slithering – completely out of control! And you should have seen the looks on the faces of the other animals as Tortoise zoomed through them, mud spraying up behind as he shot away!

And you should have seen him as he came hurtling down between the flags at breakneck speed until he swooshed across the winning line and came to a halt right in the centre of the stadium!

The crowd went mad!

They cheered and roared and yelled and screamed and chanted Tortoise's name.

'We love you, Tortoise! We love you, Tortoise!'

He stood up in the centre of the arena and thought his heart was going to burst with joy!

Tortoise could hardly believe it was happening to him.

He was still in a daze at the closing ceremony that night when, beneath a beautiful golden moon, Badger presented the medals.

To Hare for the running.

To Frog for the jumping.

To Squirrel for throwing the stone.

And to Tortoise for ski-ing down the muddy slope.

And as each winner leaned forward to have the medal hung round his neck, the six mice – dressed in bright scarlet uniforms – trumpeted out their praise.

As the last notes from the final fanfare bounced away into the forest, Tortoise looked up at the sky, and sighed with pure happiness.

Emil Pacholek

A street of cats

The street was short and narrow, hardly more than a lane. At the end by the market square, it was tidy and respectable, but it got rapidly shabbier until at the end by the canal it really wasn't a nice street at all. It was called Pig Lane, and there were only seven houses, all on the same side of the road. On the other side there was a high fence, and behind the fence was a vacant lot overgrown with coarse grass and brambles. The people of the town dumped rubbish there; old iron bedsteads and broken-down bicycles and even worn-out cars. It made a lovely place for the children to play, but the more respectable people said it was a disgrace and why wasn't something done about it?

One day a factory was to be built there, and it said so on a large, weather-beaten sign. But no one knew when that day would come, and in the meantime the children played, and dogs raced and barked and dug holes.

But when darkness fell and the dogs and children went home, the vacant lot was taken over by the cats.

Every house in Pig Lane had its cat. In the best house, at the market square end, lived a Siamese called Chi Ki. His owners kept a ladies' hairdressing establishment. They were out all day, which made it very lonely for Chi Ki, who was left shut up indoors.

At No. 2 there was a marmalade tom cat whose name was Ginger. Two old ladies owned him and loved him a great deal more than he loved them. Ginger was very independent and had a poor opinion of women.

The cat at No. 3 was a tabby called Martha. Her owner was a long-distance truck driver who was away a great deal. His wife hated cats, and only let Martha live there because she was such a good ratter. Rats came out from the canal banks and terrified the women in Pig Lane. Martha caught a rat nearly every night, so she was allowed to remain.

Beyond No. 3 the houses were on the down-grade. Gone were the shining windows and neat gravel paths of Nos. 1, 2, and 3. No. 4 and No. 5 were joined together and both had shabby brickwork and flaking paint. The gates hung crookedly on their hinges and grass forced its way through the concrete of the front paths.

At No. 4 lived Snowy, the sweetest, gentlest old cat imaginable. She never had a bad thought or did an unkind action. She couldn't even bring herself to kill rats. She belonged to an old man who lived alone and cooked for himself in a messy, untidy sort of way.

No. 5 was the home of Pete, a black kitten with a white shirt front who led a miserable life. He was constantly being pulled about and teased by a little horror of a boy to whom he had been given for Christmas. Pete was rapidly developing a very bad temper, which was not surprising. He was an extremely unhappy little cat.

House No. 6 was in the last stages of decay, with broken windows mended with cardboard and a door which never quite shut. It belonged to a sailor – who was hardly ever at home – and his wife and daughter. The cat, Sam, was a Manx and had no tail. This was not the result of an accident, it was the way he was born. No true Manx cat has a tail, and they spend all their lives trying to make people believe it, which sours them. No one, least of all a cat, likes jokes made about his appearance.

The seventh house, right down on the canal bank, was really hardly a house at all. It was a shack, and a disgrace to the town. It was occupied by an old man who bought rags and bones. He went around the town with a very old pony and cart, and brought back loads of rubbish to sort over in his backyard. His cat was a huge grey tom, scarred all over from fighting, with half an ear missing and only one good eye. His name was Pyewacket, and he was the smartest, most cunning cat in the whole street and the whole town and probably in the whole world.

Rosemary Weir

The dragonfly

There was once a terrible monster
lived in a pond, deep under the water.

Brown as mud he was, in the mud he hid,
among murk of reed-roots, sodden twigs,
with his long hungry belly,
six legs for creeping,
eyes like headlights
awake or sleeping;
but he was not big.

A tiddler came to sneer and jeer
and flaunt his flashing tail –
Ugly old stick-in-the mud
couldn't catch a snail!
I'm not scared –
when, like a shot,
two pincers nab him, and he's got!

For the monster's jaw hides a clawed stalk
like the arm of a robot, a dinner fork,
that's tucked away cunningly till the last minute –
shoots out – and back with a victim in it!

Days, weeks, months, two years and beyond,
fear of the monster beset the pond;
he lurked, grabbed, grappled, gobbled and grew,
ambushing always somewhere new –

Who saw him last? Does anyone know?
Don't go near the mud! But I must go!
Keep well away from the rushes! But how?
Has anyone seen my brother? Not for a week now –
he's been eaten
for certain!

And then, one day, it was June, they all saw him.
He was coming slowly up out of the mud,
they stopped swimming. No one dared
approach, attack. They kept back.

Up a tall reed they saw him climbing
higher and higher, until
he broke the surface, climbing still.

There he stopped, in the wind and the setting sun.
We're safe at last! they cried. *He's gone!*
What became of the monster, was he ill, was he sad?
Was nobody sorry? Had he crept off to die? Was he mad?

Not one of them saw how, suddenly,
as if an invisible knife had touched his back,
he has split, split completely –
his head split like a lid!
The cage is open. Slowly he comes through,
an emperor, with great eyes burning blue.

He rests there, veils of silver a cloak for him.
Night and the little stars travel the black pond,
and now, first light of the day,
his shining cloak wide wings, a flash, a whirr,
a jewelled helicopter,
he's away!

O fully he had served his time,
shunned and unlovely in the drab slime,
for freedom at the end – for the sky –
dazzling hunter, Dragonfly!

Libby Houston

The blue whale

She was one of the largest animals in the world and she was lonely; for she had seen no other of her kind for four years. Now, nearly five years old, she was quite grown up and she wanted a mate to live with for the rest of her life. She made her strange calls over and over again. Then she listened for an answer – but none came.

The blue whale had spent every winter in the warm South Pacific Ocean; and every summer she had moved south into the waters of the Antarctic. She had mixed with other whales; but they were different – finbacks, humpbacks, and sometimes sperm whales. She listened to their sounds and understood some of them; but she knew they were not her kind.

The blue whale's cries could be heard as far as 640 kilometres away. The blue whale called again and again, but none of her own kind answered. She flipped up to the surface and joined a school of dolphins merrily playing in the waves. They accepted her and included her in their play. All that winter she swam in the Pacific. It was near the end of winter when she heard an answering call. It was one of her kind – a bull. He was 600 kilometres away when he first heard her. He immediately sent out his reply call and turned his huge body in her direction. She also turned and swam towards him, each whale homing on the other's call. All night they swam under the sea; and hour by hour their calls grew louder. Then, in the early morning, they sighted each other. The bull whale was thirty metres long and she thought he looked beautiful. For two hours they played together, swimming, diving, huffing, blowing, sliding, bumping and rubbing.

Later that year the blue whale gave birth to her calf underwater. She taught the baby how to breathe, roll and swim. After six months the calf was fifteen metres long and he could move almost as fast as his parents. It was time to go to the Antarctic where the summer sun was beginning to melt some of the ice. The calf always travelled close to his mother for he was still a baby – and whenever there was time, mother and calf played in the water, diving deep and racing to the surface, all the time making strange whale noises of happiness.

Mother and son were playing happily together when the lookout on the whale-catcher spotted them. The crew of the ship had not seen a whale for three days and they were anxious to earn a bonus. There was an international agreement not to kill blue whales because they had been hunted almost to extinction. But who was to know what kind of whale they hunted in the lonely icy sea? The gunner captain sounded the alarm bell and in minutes the crew were all at action stations on the catcher. The bull and cow saw the black and white catcher bearing down on them and they knew what it was from previous experience. But the calf thought the catcher was something to play with – just as the captain expected; and when the calf plunged towards the ship, his mother went after him to head him off, all the time making frantic 'come back' sounds. The bull came up and tried to get between them and the catcher; then he turned away to try and draw off the catcher and so give the cow and calf chance to escape.

'Follow the cow and calf,' the gunner shouted to the helmsman. He knew that the bull would come back to protect his family. The gunner was almost near enough to get the cow in his sights. The bull dived and turned to rejoin the cow and calf. They were together again, with the calf safe between father and mother, and all three dived deep to escape the killer boat.

Deep, deep they dived and on the surface the catcher cut engine speed and waited. The whales had to rise and blow. All three broke surface together – all within range of the gunner. He sighted his harpoon gun on the cow and fired. The long, thick nylon cord flew up in a great arc; but the harpoon missed the cow and plunged into the bull. It struck deep into his back and the grenades in the harpoon nose exploded, shattering the bull's insides. He thrashed the water in agony and dived deep with the harpoon still holding and blood pouring out of his shattered body. The gunner cursed because he thought the cow would

escape with the calf; but she didn't, she came to help
the bull. For two hours the bull fought, with the
cow and calf frantically trying to help. When
the bull's great heart finally gave out, they
winched him to the surface. The cow
came alongside and, with her flipper,
tried to pull her mate down into the
safety of the sea. It was no good. She knew
that he was dead; and now she must get the
calf away. The heartbroken cow kept her calf
close as they swam between the icebergs. They were just clearing a group
of icebergs when the look-out on the catcher spotted them. 'There they are,'
he shouted. The chase was on.

One hour later, the gunner had the cow in his sights and the killer
harpoon was launched. She cried out as the harpoon struck and screamed
as the explosive charge shattered her guts. She thrashed to the surface and
then dived. The sea was dyed with her blood. The calf kept with her,
making his calls, but his mother could no longer hear him. She came to the
surface exhausted. The calf came alongside and with his flipper tried to
pull her down to the safety of the sea just as she had done with her mate.
Again and again the calf rolled over and slapped his flipper on his mother's
bloodstained body but it was no good; and all the time the catcher crew
winched in her broken body. She blew for the last time and she blew red
blood from her lungs. Then she died in a final flurry with her great tail
lashing the water; and the calf still stayed alongside trying to push his dead
mother down with his flipper – deep down under the sea away from the
killer ship. A seaman attached a long tube to the dead cow and air was
pumped into her body so that she could be floated and left for the towing
boat to pick up later.

Now the harpoon had been reloaded and the gunner got his sights on the
calf. He fired just as the calf plunged deeply. 'Missed him,' said the gunner.

The calf swam right under the catcher and stayed underwater until he
reached the icebergs. The catcher went back to the factory ship. Three hours
later, the calf went back to the body of his mother and just circled round and
round blowing and nudging her with his flipper. He was still doing it when
the towing boat appeared. When he saw the boat, the calf was panic-
stricken and instinctively did what his father and mother had done: he
went towards the boat and tried to lead the crew away from his mother. The
seamen had seen it all before and they just laughed at him. A man put a steel
cable around the body of the cow and then the carcase was towed towards
the factory ship sixty kilometres away. The calf followed his dead mother,

crying his sad call all the time. Then he heard the great factory ship and in fear he turned and swam away. He went on and on through the icebergs, calling and calling. He heard no answer and perhaps he never would because so few blue whales were left in the oceans of the world.

Frank Pinfold

The boy and the swan

Between the cottage where the boy and the old woman lived, and the town where he went to school, there was a wide, flat expanse of water, a small estuary, where a little river ran down to meet the sea. Every day the boy trod the bridge that carried the road over the water, once in the morning on his way to school, once in the afternoon on his way back. Sometimes he stopped on the bridge to watch the water crawling sluggishly beneath his feet; sometimes he went down on to the grass bank and leaned down to try to catch minnows in his hands. If he looked upstream from the bridge, he often saw fishermen, anglers, sitting with their rods and lines, their umbrellas and their baskets, at the point where the river ran deeper, and he thought how cold they must be and wondered whether they caught anything to make their vigil worthwhile.

It occurred to him that perhaps he could catch something which would be a welcome addition to their diet. He had read in story-books that it was possible to catch fish with bait on a bent pin, a long stick and a length of string. But this spring, when he looked up the river from the bridge, he did not see the usual line of anglers waiting patiently for a catch, and one afternoon, when the sun had a little more warmth than it had had for the last months, and the wind blew soft from the south, the boy walked up the river and round the bend which hid its upper reaches from the bridge, to find out where the anglers had gone, and to make up his mind where he himself should try to fish if he meant to make the attempt. There were trees here, and the river meandered in curves like a snake, flowing quietly over the flat ground, and sometimes expanding sideways into backwaters where the water was still and surrounded by rushes and reeds. He had turned aside

to look more closely at one of them, and was just about to leave, finding the main river more interesting, when there was a movement on the further side of the water, and out from the reeds came a pair of swans. They swam so smoothly that they seemed to glide, as if they were propelled by magic. Their great white bodies floated on the surface of the pool and were reflected below them, so that each swan seemed to have another, an exact double, swimming upside down beneath it. They came out to the middle of the pond, side by side, a royal couple, sometimes dipping their long elegant necks down into the water, so that they left only their bodies, like two vast feathered eggs, in sight.

At school, the boy had seen a video film about swans. It had shown a couple swimming side by side, preening each other's plumage like this. It had shown the swans building a nest, raising their young. It had also shown the fate of swans which had been choked by the hooks of anglers and poisoned by the lead weights used at the end of the fishing line. It had been a sad film in some ways, but the boy had seen people who spent their time trying to rescue the swans from the dangers that threatened them. He hadn't taken very much notice of the video at the time, but now that he saw these birds close to, for himself, he knew that he hated the fishermen whose carelessness was killing grand creatures like this couple. As he gazed now, the swans raised their heads from the water, turned towards each other, and each, with its bill, groomed the feathers of the other. The boy saw that this was a courtship. The pair were caressing each other.

The boy knew, for the first time in his life, that what he was looking at was beautiful. Something inside his chest hurt and turned over and his throat was tight. He was angry with himself. It was stupid to have feelings like this, just about a couple of big birds.

But he stayed, watching them, for a long time. He watched them searching for food at the bottom of the pond. He watched them swim away and back again. He saw one swan go out on to the muddy edge of the pond, walking with an ungainly, flat-footed gait which did not suit its majestic progress on water. Presently the other swan followed into the reeds, and then the boy remembered that he was supposed to be on his way home, and he went quickly back to the bridge and the road, and ran part of the way back so that the old woman should not scold him.

After this, he went often up the river to the little backwater. He liked watching the swans. He had given up his intention to fish, and there were no other anglers to remind him. He spent as long as he could, crouching or lying among the reeds, watching the swans. There was only one pair, he discovered, on this particular stretch of the river. And because he never saw anyone else in the backwater, he began to believe that no one but he had ever visited it, and that no one else knew about this one pair. There were plenty of other swans on other reaches of the estuary, but this couple were separate from the others, just as he was separate from the other children in his school. If he had known what the word meant, he might have said that he loved the swans.

When he had been watching them for nearly a month, he went to the teacher who looked after the school library.

'I want a book about birds,' he said, careful not to mention the word 'swan' in case someone discovered his secret.

She was surprised. This boy had never asked her for a book before.

'What sort of book? A story book? Or an information book?'

'I want a book that tells about what birds do.'

'You mean their habits and habitat?'

He did not understand the word 'habitat', and she explained. 'Where they live and build their nests. What sort of country you'd find them in.'

He agreed, and she gave him a book called *British Birds*. It was full of coloured pictures and he was surprised to find how many birds he knew by sight, though he had known the names of only a few. Sparrow. Blackbird. Robin. But the book told him that he had also seen swallows and martins and fieldfares and blue tits and kestrels and others which spent the winter in the bleak country where he lived because it was less cold than the far north from which they came. He was pleased by this, but disappointed in what he found about swans. Two paragraphs described the rivers and ponds where swans were to be found, their eating and nesting habits, their plumage, their flight. The picture of the swan was boring, flat. It didn't give the impression it should have of the silver majesty of his swans. He took the book back to the library without enthusiasm.

'Interesting?' the teacher asked him, as he handed her the volume.

He lied. 'Yes.' Then, needing to know more, he asked, 'What does "mute" mean?'

'Mute?' she asked, puzzled.

'It says "The Mute Swan".'

'Oh, yes. Means it doesn't sing. It hasn't a proper song like other birds. Not like... a blackbird. Or a nightingale.'

'You mean it's dumb?' He was disappointed.

'They say it sings just once, when it's going to die. Right at the end.'

The boy was enthralled. This was magic. He imagined those lovely creatures lifting their long curved necks and opening their powerful throats to let out a song such as no other bird could ever achieve. He did not know what it would be like, but because the swan is such a large bird, he thought it would be more startling and more brilliant than any bird-song in the world. And if you sing only once in your life, it must surely be a very special last song?

'Anything else?' the librarian was asking him.

He said, 'No,' then remembered something else that had puzzled him. 'It says in the book that swans mate for life. What does that mean?'

'What it says. They stay as one pair. Husband and wife. They don't change. They stay... married... to each other till they die.'

The boy thought about this too. On his way home that afternoon, he wondered what happened if one of the swan pair died. Could the one that was left find another mate? But he did not ask any more. He did not like asking questions, he preferred to wait until he could find things out for himself. But he was troubled by the idea of a single lonely swan. He went up the river then to look at his swans, to make sure that they were there, safely together. He saw them floating serenely on the water, their reflections bright in the afternoon spring sun. He was comforted. They were together. All was well.

Catherine Storr

MY WORLD

Paul the painter

When Grandpa came for Paul at school
He saw how the dolls weren't able
To move their arms or stretch their legs
As they lay packed tight in the cradle

After they'd feasted on sausage pie,
Chips and ice-cream for their tea
Grandpa said, 'I've a special job
Where I want you to work with me.'

In the spare bedroom cupboard
Was a cot with room for a baby,
A strong wooden cot that had been bright blue
But now was dusty and dingy.

Paul helped Grandpa sandpaper
Till the work was smooth and level
And then he opened a tin of paint
And they painted it white together.

The cot still had squiggles and dribbles
And still looked worn and old
But they made it look new and beautiful
By spraying it all over with gold.

Grandma made a mattress and blanket
And when they took the cot to school
Children and teachers admired it
And the dolls had plenty of room.

There were spray and paint left over
And as Paul fell asleep that night
He thought of the houses, bridges and ghosts
Waiting to be painted gold and white.

Stanley Cook

photocopiable

Harriet's temper

One afternoon, when Harriet came home from school, she was very cross.

'I want to play with Melissa,' she said in a grumpy voice. 'I want to.'

'Not now,' said her mum, 'it's too late. It's tea-time now and then it'll be bedtime.'

Harriet was so cross that she could feel herself go hot inside and her tummy began to gurgle. She stomped and stamped around the house. She shouted so loudly that she almost knocked her dad flat.

'I WANT TO PLAY WITH MELISSA,' she screamed. The words were so big and fat when they jumped out of her mouth that they bounced around the room bumping into the furniture.

'Please stop shouting Harriet,' said her dad, 'you're going to blow the house down.'

Harriet didn't stop shouting. She shouted the baked beans into her tea, she shouted the bubbles into her bath, she shouted her teddy into her bed and she shouted the dreams into her sleep.

'I know what her trouble is,' said her mum, 'she's lost her temper.'

And she had. She shouted all through the night and was still shouting when she woke up.

Then the neighbours began to complain.

'Can't you keep that girl quiet?' said Mr Sharp. 'I didn't sleep a wink last night.'

'Can't you keep that girl quiet?' said Mrs Sharp. 'She's disturbing my pigeons.'

'And the cat and the goldfish,' said Mr Sharp.

'And all of us,' said Harriet's mum and dad and sister.

'What you need is the Temper Police,' said Mrs Sharp.

'I'll call them,' said her big sister Lizzie, 'right now.'

Quick as you like PC Bobbin was at the door.

'Now then,' he said. 'PC Bobbin of the Temper Police here, lost our temper have we?'

'Yes,' said Harriet's mum.

'NO!' shouted Harriet.

'Oh,' said PC Bobbin.

'She has,' said her dad, 'just listen.'

'NO I HAVE NOT,' screamed Harriet. This time her scream was so loud it knocked the policeman's helmet right off and he had to bend down and pick it up.

'Now then,' he said, taking out a notebook and a pencil. 'How old is this temper?'

'It's five,' said Harriet's mum.

'NO IT'S NOT,' said Harriet.

'Yes it is,' said her dad, 'because you're five.'

'NO I'M NOT,' shouted Harriet.

'Yes she is,' said Lizzie to the policeman.

'What shape is it?' he asked. 'What size? What colour?'

'It's round like a marble, not very big and it's golden and red and blue,' said her mother.

'When was it lost? Where was it lost? What sound does it make?' he asked.

'She lost it yesterday afternoon when we walked home from school,' said her mum.

'It goes WAAAAAA!' said Lizzie helpfully.

'But only when its lost,' said her dad, 'otherwise it's sweet.'

'And where is it usually kept?' asked PC Bobbin.

'In my smile, in my eyes, in my tummy, in my tongue,' said Harriet. 'BUT NOW IT'S LOST!'

'Well, well, well,' said PC Bobbin. 'We must find it. We can't have a lost temper running around all over the place. That would never do.'

'I WANT MY TEMPER BACK,' screamed Harriet. 'RIGHT NOW.'

'So do we,' groaned her mum and dad and Lizzie.

They all set off at once with PC Bobbin to look for the temper. They asked the post woman, the milkman, the dustman and the woman who delivered the free newspapers. They asked Mr and Mrs Buttons the butchers, and Mr and Mrs Garden the greengrocers. They went to the newspaper shop and asked Mr Patel, but he didn't know. They asked the two girls who worked there with him and they didn't know either.

'We'll put a note in the shop door,' said Mr Patel. '"Lost, one temper. Please ask inside for details." You never know, it might turn up.'

'NO IT WON'T,' sobbed Harriet. 'AND I WANT IT BACK... NOW!'

At every shop she kicked and screamed, argued and raged. In the butcher's shop she wanted sweets. In the greengrocer's shop she wanted pork pie. In Mr Patel's shop she wanted plums and apples. In the baker's shop she wanted a comic and in the post office she wanted a sticky bun. She was in a terrible state.

'I WANT... I WANT... I WANT... EVERYTHING,' she yelled. 'NOW!'

'I NEED... I NEED... I NEED... EVERYTHING,' she screeched. 'NOW!'

'I MUST HAVE... MUST... DADDY... MUMMY... I MUST HAVE EVERYTHING,' she wailed. 'NOW!

Harriet's temper was so badly lost that PC Bobbin enlisted the help of seven other police officers, a fire engine and its crew, Harriet's teacher Mrs Walker and Mr Richardson the window cleaner, as well as Mum and Dad and Lizzie.

All of them looked everywhere. They looked high. They looked low. They looked in narrow places and in wide places. They looked in dry places and in wet places. They looked in muddy places, sticky places, cold places and hot places. They looked in round places, square places, smooth places and rough places. They looked in keyholes, sinks, cupboards and drainpipes. They looked in up-in-the-air places and down-holes-in-the-ground places. They even looked in Mr Richardson's bucket, but Harriet's temper could not be found.

'I HATE THIS,' she yelled. 'I FEEL

HORRID. I FEEL NASTY. I FEEL LIKE I'VE SWALLOWED A SLUG, EATEN AN EARWIG, MUNCHED UP A MAGGOT, GULPED DOWN A GRUB. I HATE IT!'

That night her dad tried hard to read Harriet a story. Harriet kept saying 'NO' to every book he tried to read. After the tenth book he said, 'That's it, I'm going downstairs. I'm going to switch your light off and you can go to sleep.'

'NO DADDY,' she wailed. 'NO-O-O-O. DADDY I... I....' At that moment something small and smooth about the size of a marble, but coloured red, gold and blue fizzed out from under her pillow and into Harriet's mouth. She swallowed and she smiled.

'Daddy,' she said, 'I've got it back, it's in my tummy again.' She clapped her hands, smiled again and fell fast asleep.

From that day on Harriet tried very hard never to lose her temper again. Once or twice she did but she always knew just where to find it.

David Harmer

I hate Mark and Gemma

My name's Chris. I've always been the littlest in our family. That's 'cause I'm the youngest – my brother Mark's years older than me, and my sister Gemma's even older than Mark. However much I grow, I never catch up with Mark and Gemma.

My feet wouldn't reach the pedals of the tandem we had for Christmas. A tandem's a bike, a special bike like two bikes stuck together so that two people can ride it. It has two saddles and everything.

'It's a present for you to share,' Mum said.

Share! That's a joke. Mark and Gemma never share. They grab everything and they're stronger than me, and can run faster.

'Scaredy cat, scaredy cat, can't catch me!' they yell, and if it's sweets they've grabbed they stay just out of reach and cram them into their mouths as fast as they can, laughing so much they can hardly swallow. And if we're in the car with Mum and Dad they make me sit on the lumpy bit in the middle where I can't see out and I feel sick. That's not fair, is it?

I hate Mark and Gemma. I wish there was just me, but I still wouldn't be able to ride the tandem 'cause it's too big.

That tandem had to go. That was all I could think. It had to go. It was me or it. It was bad enough before, but I stood no chance against Mark and Gemma on wheels. I would be patient, bide my time, and then I would strike!

One day after tea, when everybody was watching telly, I slipped out of the back door with the key to the shed burning in my pocket. It was already getting dark. I wanted it to be black as pitch, as dark as the cellar, but I'm afraid of the dark. Mark and Gemma have told me about the spooks and goblins that come out at night looking for people to eat. Little people like me.

The key to the shed was stiff in the lock and hurt my fingers, and the door dragged on the ground when I opened it, making a noise like a cement mixer. But no one came.

I could hardly see the tandem, all tangled up with Dad's big bike. It was so heavy, I scraped my shins and crushed my fingers getting it out of the shed. I was going to take it to the woods at the end of the road, but halfway there I dropped it. It crashed into the road, clanging like a dustbin and nearly falling on top of me. I pulled with all my strength but I couldn't get it upright again. So I ran home and slipped in at the back door before anybody saw me.

I didn't sleep that night for fear that someone would burst in on me, and grab me and shout, 'The tandem! Where's the tandem? You did it! We know you did it!'

But no one came. Still, I was beginning to wish that I hadn't done it.

At breakfast everybody acted as if nothing had happened.

'Don't gobble your cereal, Chris,' Mum said.

'Chris's a pig,' said Gemma.

'A little pig,' said Mark.

I hate them! When Mum's back was turned I flicked milk at Mark with my spoon. He ducked and it hit Dad who was just coming through the door.

'Animals!' he yelled.

'It was Chris,' said Gemma.

'Chris done it,' said Mark.

'Chris done it! Chris done it!' That's all I ever hear! Well, this time Chris had really done it. And by the time I was running to school I was glad again.

When I got back from school there was nobody at home. Dad was still at work, but there was usually somebody there.

I let myself in with the key we keep under the flower pot in the yard – for the burglars, Dad says – and made myself a doorstep of bread and jam. Nobody came.

Where was everybody? They must have found out about the tandem! Were they all at the police station?

When Mum came back I was watching TV.

'What's for tea?' I asked.

'Just wait until your dad gets home,' she said, taking off her coat and disappearing into the kitchen. I stayed in front of the TV, but I didn't see much. I was too busy thinking about what would happen when Dad got home.

Mark and Gemma came in with Dad. They all had that look which said that something was going on. Gemma and Mark kept looking at each other and bursting into giggles. They knew about the tandem!

Tea tasted like sawdust, though everybody else seemed to enjoy it. I hardly touched mine. I thought I was going to be sick.

'What's the matter with you, Chris?' Mum asked. 'Are you sick?'

Dad said, 'I want to talk to you, Chris.'

This was it. I'd had it. They knew it was me!

Dad put his hand on my shoulder. 'Come and see what's outside.'

My knees turned to jelly. A car must have run over the tandem. It would be a mess of tangled metal.

Gemma and Mark pushed me and pulled me. 'Come on, Titch!' they shouted.

I wasn't going to cry, not in front of Mark and Gemma. What I wanted to do was to run upstairs and get away from everybody, but instead I found myself outside in the back yard and looking at a shiny new bike. A little bike. For one person. A person about my size.

'It's for you,' said Dad. 'Because you're too small for the tandem — hey, Mark! Get off that bike! It's Chris's!'

I just stood there, not knowing what to say. Then I found my voice, a kind of croak.

'I can't ride it.'

'I'll teach you.' Dad pulled Mark off the bike and wheeled it up to me. 'Look, it's got these stabilisers to make it easy at first. But you won't need those for long.'

It was like flying. I was a bit wobbly at first, but then I was out of the garden and off down the road, swooping and soaring like a bird. The wheels went chunk-chunk, chunk-chunk across the joins in the pavement. Pedestrians jumped when I came up behind them and rang my bell. I was free!

But not for long.

When I got back the house was in uproar. Mum was crying and Gemma and Mark were looking scared. Dad came out of the shed. I'd been so in love with my new bike that I hadn't noticed the open shed door.

'They must have picked the lock. There's no sign of a break-in,' Dad said.

My heart sank to my boots. This was the end. When they found out that I had taken the tandem nobody would talk to me ever again.

Dad shook his head. 'Funny they didn't take my bike as well.'

Mum wiped her face on her sleeve and gave me a hug. 'At least you've still got your bike, Chris.'

I ran upstairs, got into bed and hid under the bedclothes.

What was I going to do? I couldn't stay at home. When they found out I'd taken the tandem I'd be put in prison. I couldn't bear to see Mum crying or hear Dad shouting. I had to run away.

There was an old piece of cheese in the fridge, and some wrinkly apples in the bowl. I put them in my pocket.

The moon was full and the night was as light as a dark day. Already I was shivering. I'd never been any further than the woods before on my own. The goblins would get me! Or the spooky ghosts!

My new bike was in the hall where I'd left it. A criminal like me didn't deserve it. I walked. At first I knew the roads, where they went, how to get home. Then there were streets I recognised, but didn't really know. Things looked so different at night. Then everything was strange and I was lost. I couldn't go back any more.

I ran. Past houses, shops, schools I ran, along roads and over bridges. The echo of my feet sounded like somebody chasing me, and I ran faster.

Suddenly I was tired and hungry. I ate my cheese and my apple. They made me thirsty. Rain started to fall and I held my head back and let the water trickle slowly into my mouth. It was salty with tears.

When I lowered my head I saw a police car pulled up at the kerb beside me. I was going to be arrested! I tried to run but my legs wouldn't work. They felt like tree trunks.

A policewoman in uniform got out of the car. She came over to me and said, 'Hallo.'

'I give myself up,' I tried to say, but the words came out all hoarse and squeaky.

The policewoman bent down and put her arm round me. I was shaking with cold.

'I think you'd better come with us, don't you?'

The ride in the Panda car, the radio messages to and fro, the police station, the questions from strangers – all these exciting things went by in a blur. My wet clothes were taken away and I was wrapped in blankets and given hot soup. By the time my parents came I was asleep.

When I woke up I was in my own bed. Lying there, warm and snug with the familiar sounds of the house coming up the stairs, the cold wet streets were like a dream. Just for a moment it seemed I was running, running again. In a fright I jumped out of bed and landed with a thump on the floor. Then I was wide awake. I was home.

I went to the window. Gemma and Mark were riding the tandem out in the yard. They saw me at the window, and laughed and waved.

Mum came into the bedroom. She put her arms round me and held me tight.

'We were so worried! You must never run away again!'

'The tandem....'

'Mark and Gemma found it in the road and hid it. They were very silly and they've had a good talking to.'

'I took it.'

'So that was it. You've been very naughty too. Why did you take the tandem?'

'Because... just because.' I couldn't tell Mum that I hated Mark and Gemma. I was confused. Even knowing how they'd tricked me, I didn't know if I hated them any more. Last night I'd missed them like anything.

'Because you couldn't ride it? Well you must never do that again either.' Mum smiled and hugged me even tighter. 'I won't tell anybody. It will be our secret. The important thing is that you're back home again, safe and sound.'

And she was right.

Alan Brown

Cheese, peas and chocolate pudding

There was once a little boy who ate cheese, peas and chocolate pudding. Cheese, peas and chocolate pudding. Cheese, peas and chocolate pudding. Every day the same old things: cheese, peas and chocolate pudding.

For breakfast he would have some cheese. Any kind. Cream cheese, American cheese, Swiss cheese, Dutch cheese, Italian cheese, blue cheese, green cheese, yellow cheese, brick cheese. Just cheese for breakfast.

For lunch he ate peas. Green or yellow peas. Frozen peas, canned peas, dried peas, split peas, black-eyed peas. No potatoes, though – just peas for lunch.

And for supper he would have cheese and peas. And chocolate pudding. Cheese, peas and chocolate pudding. Cheese, peas and chocolate pudding. Every day the same old things: cheese, peas and chocolate pudding.

Once his mother bought a lamb chop for him. She cooked it in a little frying pan on the stove, and she put some salt on it, and gave it to the little boy on a little blue dish. The boy looked at it. He smelled it. (It did smell delicious!) He even touched it. But....

'Is this cheese?' he asked.

'It's a lamb chop, darling,' said his mother.

The boy shook his head. 'Cheese!' he said. So his mother ate the lamb chop herself, and the boy had some cottage cheese.

One day his big brother was chewing a raw carrot. It sounded so good, the little boy reached his hand out for a bite.

'Sure!' said his brother. 'Here!' The little boy *almost* put the carrot in his mouth, but at the last minute he remembered, and he said, 'Is this peas?'

'No, fella, it's a carrot,' said his brother.

'Peas,' said the little boy firmly, handing the carrot back.

Once his daddy was eating a big dish of raspberry jelly. It looked so shiny red and cool, the little boy came over and held his mouth open.

'Want a taste?' asked his daddy. The little boy looked and looked at the jelly. He almost looked it off the dish. But: 'Is it chocolate pudding?' he asked.

'No, son, it's jelly,' said his daddy.

So the little boy frowned and backed away. 'Chocolate pudding!'he said.

His grandma baked cookies for him. 'Nope!' said the boy.

His grandpa bought him an ice-cream cone. The little boy just shook his head.

His aunt and uncle invited him for a fried-chicken dinner. Everybody ate fried chicken and more fried chicken. Except the little boy. And you know what he ate.

Cheese, peas and chocolate pudding. Cheese, peas and chocolate pudding. Every day the same old things: cheese, peas and chocolate pudding.

But one day – ah, one day, a very funny thing happened. The little boy was playing puppy. He lay on the floor and growled and barked and rolled over. He crept to the table where his big brother was having lunch.

'Arf-arf!' he barked.

'Good doggie!' said his brother, patting his head. The little boy lay down on his back on the floor and barked again.

But at that minute, his big brother dropped a piece of *something* from his plate. And the little boy's mouth was just ready to say 'Arf!' And what do you think happened?

Something dropped into the little boy's mouth. He sat up in surprise. Because *something* was on his tongue. And *something* was warm and juicy and delicious!

And it didn't taste like cheese. And it did *not* taste like peas. And it certainly wasn't chocolate pudding.

The little boy chewed slowly. Each chew tasted better than the last. He swallowed *something* and opened his mouth again. Wide. As wide as he could.

'Want some more?' asked his brother.

The little boy closed his mouth and thought. 'That's not cheese,' he said.

'No, it's not,' said his brother.

'And it isn't peas.'

'No, not peas,' said his brother.

'And it couldn't be chocolate pudding.'

'No, it certainly is not chocolate pudding,' smiled his brother. 'It's hamburger.'

The little boy thought hard. 'I like hamburger,' he said.

So his big brother shared the rest of his hamburger with the little boy, and ever after that, guess what!

Ever after that, the little boy ate cheese, peas, and chocolate pudding and hamburger.

Until he was your age, of course. When he was your age, he ate everything.

Betty Van Witsen

Hide and shriek!

A wardrobe sits fat and alone
OR IS IT?
For suddenly a door
like a bird's wing, flaps softly open.
Now slowly a hand of fingers
pretending to be spiders' legs creep round into view.
The hand is followed by a green troused leg
which hangs there as if unsure of where to go.
The wardrobe door now looks as if it has grown
one spidery hand and one green leg.
Next a watchful pair of eyes
with a silvery smile hanging below them,
slide out from the wardrobe
and its dark secrets.

A young girl now stands still in front of the wardrobe.
A young girl called Amy, stands still
and... listens.
At first she hears only the clock tick-ticking on the wall.
The television rumble-grumbling in the front room.
The washing machine spin-winning in the kitchen.
But then her ears are quick to catch hold of another sound.
A floor board sneak-creaking under someone's foot!
Amy's silvery smile slips back inside her mouth
as she disappears into the darkest piece of wardrobe
and... waits.

Outside in the hallway at the top of the stairs,
Amy's brother Tom, is on the hunt.
All week Amy and Tom have been playing their game
of 'Hide and shriek'.
Amy hides and Tom has, not only to find her,
but make her SHRIEK at the same time.
Tom creeps towards his mum and dad's bedroom
trying to walk on the carpet without letting it know.
He reaches the door and shakes hands with it
then Tom and the door tiptoe into the bedroom.
Inside the wardrobe a hanger rattles,
a shoe topples and a mouth giggles.

Tom stops and thinks.
He needs a new way of attacking the wardrobe.
He needs a new way of making Amy shriek.
On Monday he had come in and announced
he was going to push the wardrobe over.
Amy hadn't believed him
until he had started banging on its sides
and trying to rock it.
Amy had soon leapt from the wardrobe SCREAMING!
On Tuesday he had stood outside the wardrobe
and told Amy he had collected creepy crawlies from the garden.
He then opened the wardrobe door
and lobbed in a collection of spiders, flies and nasties.
They were plastic of course!
Amy again had shot from the wardrobe YELLING!
On Wednesday he had said he had given up
and pretended to leave the room.
When Amy had eventually crept out
he Jack-in-a-boxed from behind the wardrobe
and thundered 'BOO'.
Amy had sprinted from the room SCREECHING!
But yesterday had been the best so far.
He'd switched out the lights
and climbed on top of the wardrobe.
There he began to make moaning, groaning noises
and when Amy opened the wardrobe door
Tom dangled a skeleton in front of her.
It was fluorescent and made of cardboard of course.
Amy had jumped from the room HOWLING!

'But now for today!' thinks Tom.
First he slides towards the curtains and closes them.
Then it's lights off.

A quick, flick and a click does the trick!
Next he slips out a torch
and then uses its arm of light
to help him reach the wardrobe.
Tom now stands right in front of the wardrobe's doors
and with the mixture of silence
as well as excitement bursting in his ears
he reaches forward for the handle.
A smile of triumph rides his face
as he yanks the doors open
and fires his torch into the middle of the wardrobe.

But there's a shock waiting for Tom!
For there dangling in the torch light is a body.
A body made up of one pair of green legs
hiding inside one of Dad's cardigans.
And just a clothes hanger for a head!
Tom chuckles and slowly reaches forward
to begin undoing the cardigan's buttons.
Slowly he climbs the staircase of brown buttons
until he finally reaches the top one
where he prepares to frighten his sister.
But suddenly he hears from inside the wardrobe
a deep growl of a voice
which is DEFINITELY NOT Amy's.
Tom begins to feel as if a balloon is being
blown up inside his stomach.
Meanwhile his throat tightens
as a voice begins to chant,
'There's a bogey-man, boogie-man,
And he's coming after YOU!'
With that a terrifying head shoots
out of the cardigan straight at Tom.
He staggers back, falls over and SHRIEKS,
'AAAAAAAAAAAAAAAAAGGGGGGGGHHHHHHHHHH!'
Then stampedes out of the room

Inside the wardrobe behind a plastic, horror mask
Amy's silvery smile creeps back across her face,
while from the deepest, darkest, blackest piece of wardrobe
Dad warmly whispers, 'Anyone else for 'Hide and shriek?'

Ian Souter

Copy-cat friends

Davey was six and a half and so was Jonny. They were best friends, and because their birthdays were only three weeks apart they thought of themselves almost as twins. They lived next door to each other and their mothers were also friends. Davey's mother was born and brought up near Norwich and Jonny's in Lahore, Pakistan. Davey's name was a shorter form of David. Jonny's real name was Jehangir, which means 'ruler of the world'. His big sister Razia said that it suited him perfectly since he seemed to get his own way most of the time.

Perhaps because Davey was a few weeks older than Jonny, he managed to keep half a step ahead of him in learning new things. He learned to walk and talk and to read and ride his bike just a little before Jonny did. And Jonny was always keen on following Davey. He had to have the same kind of shoes with a Velcro fastening, which made a tearing noise when you tugged at it, the same kind of blue and red anorak and the same toys that Davey had. Jonny even secretly wished that his mother would exchange her salwar-kameez for the short dresses that Mrs Hobson wore. He wished she would go into the swimming pool with him and Davey. He wished she would cook things like Yorkshire pudding and jam roly-poly which he loved to eat at Davey's. And when, shortly after his sixth birthday, his parents arranged for him to begin learning Urdu (their own language) he wouldn't go to classes. Davey didn't learn Urdu, so why should he?

His father found this all rather amusing and called him 'my little English boy', but Razia was irritated by it and thought their parents were spoiling him. 'You're a copy-cat, Jehangir Ahmad,' she would tell him, 'and you know what happens to copy-cats. They get eaten by *tigers*.' She bared her teeth and growled.

Davey's mother thought Jonny was lovely. She took the boys for walks, one on each side, and called them her twins. 'Look,' she told her friends and relations, 'one blond and one dark. Inseparable they are, too, a proper David and Jonathan.'

One day in the spring term a new craze swept Capel Cross First School. Davey and Jonny's teacher, young and energetic Miss Pinkerton, persuaded the Head (middle-aged and a trifle dusty) that writing letters was the best, if not the only, way to get the children's work going. Miss Pinkerton was becoming a little bored with their diaries. All the children seemed to do the same things every Saturday – watching television and shopping.

'We could set up a postbox, a sorting office and a post office in the Hall,' said Miss Pinkerton enthusiastically. 'We'd get ever such good value from one project – maths and reading and language games.' She looked so keen that the Head gave in.

The first week of the letter-writing project had letters flying in all directions. The juniors wrote to the infants, the infants wrote to the top juniors and everyone wrote to the cook or the lollipop lady. Davey wrote a letter to the caretaker.

'Hey, Mum,' he chatted on the way home from school, 'guess what I wrote to Mr Ogg? Dear Mr Ogg, thank you for cleaning the bog.' And he and Jonny creased themselves laughing.

'Who's written to the two of you, then?' asked Mrs Hobson.

'I had a letter from Davey,' said Jonny.

'I had one from Jonny,' said Davey.

I wrote to the Queen and Miss Pinkerton,' said Jonny.

'I bet they won't write back, will they?' said Davey.

'Tell you what, Davey,' said his mum, 'I'll write you a letter. And I'll ask your mum to write to you, Jonny. We'll put a letter in your lunch-boxes every day.'

Next day, at lunch-time, Davey opened his lunch-box. Cheese and tomato sandwich, Hula-hoops and a Penguin. There was something else in there, too – a letter. He opened the envelope, took it out and read aloud. 'Dear Davey, I hope you are having a good time. Please finish your s-s- oh yes, sandwich. Bring home the crumbs for me to eat. See you. Love, Goldie.' He looked excitedly round the table. 'My goldfish wrote to me!'

Jonny opened his lunch-box. Jam sandwich, crisps and an apple. He had a letter as well. He smoothed it out on the crumby, sticky table. 'Hallo, Jonny, Love Amma,' he read.

From then on a note appeared every day in their lunch-boxes except once, when Mrs Hobson had a doctor's appointment, and once when Mrs Ahmad had to leave early in the morning, to look for new curtain material at the open-air market.

Sometimes Mrs Hobson wrote funny letters.

'Davey Hobson, your hair is like toffee, and I know that your ears are full of milky coffee.'

Jonny always got the same letter, 'Hallo Jonny,' or 'Hallo Jehangir, Love Amma.'

'Your mum isn't good at writing funny letters, is she?' observed Sally, who was reading over Jonny's shoulder.

Jonny didn't answer. He knew that his mother had gone to school in Pakistan and that she had been taught in Urdu, the language of Pakistan. She was learning to read and write in English with her friend Mrs Adams but it took a long time to learn a new language.

Jonny went home and complained. 'Your letters are so boring,' he told his mother. 'Everyone laughs when Davey reads his mum's letters.'

'If that's how you feel, I shan't bother writing at all,' said his mother crossly.

Jonny felt bad about being rude to his mother. He nestled his chin on her lap where she sat knitting a sweater. 'Write to me in Urdu, Amma,' he said, trying to win favour with her again. 'Then you'll be able to say all kinds of things.'

The next day at lunch-time Jonny unfolded his mum's letter. She had written beautiful, flowing Urdu letters which looked like flowering grasses and stars and raindrops showering on a window pane.

'Dear Jonny,' he pretended to read because he couldn't read a single word in Urdu. 'What's yellow and goes Slam! Slam! Slam!' He looked at his friends sitting round the table. 'A banana closing a door!'

The joke went down a treat, but Samina snatched the letter from Jonny's hand and read it for herself.

'It doesn't say that,' she shouted triumphantly. 'It's in Urdu and you can't read Urdu. It says "Dear Jonny, don't forget we are going to have tea with Aunty Rashida. Come home straight after school, Love, Amma."'

That weekend Jonny asked his mother to teach him Urdu. She bought him a blue exercise book with blank, unlined pages and a fountain pen. 'It's better to use a proper ink pen with a nib,' she explained. First he learned to write his own name, starting from the right hand side of the page and going across to the left. Then when he could do that easily she made him copy a sentence, My name is Jehangir. She made him trace it over her own writing until he could write it on his own from memory.

By the end of the summer term Jonny was reading and writing easy sentences on his own. At school, the letter-writing craze had given way to a school newspaper, but Jonny continued to get letters from his mother in his lunch-box; not every day, but quite often. They were written in Urdu and he could now read them, which he did softly, to himself. He didn't want Samina Ashraf making fun of him in front of all the others.

Now it was Davey who felt left out. He and Jonny had always done everything together, but he couldn't share Jonny's letters.

There was only one thing to do. The next Saturday morning he climbed over the wall into Jonny's garden where Mrs Ahmad was hanging out the washing.

'Aunty Firoza,' he began, addressing her in the way she preferred, 'will you teach me your language? I like the curly letters and I want to write with a real pen. Then I'll be able to read Jonny's letters and we can play spies and send each other secret messages. Will you teach me in the holidays?'

Mrs Ahmad smiled at him. 'Of course I'll teach you, Davey. After all, you and Jonny are meant to be twins, aren't you? Let's start now. Say Challo – that means "Come on".' She patted him on the head and, picking up her laundry basket, led the way indoors.

Pratima Mitchell

The brainbox

'...Now dear, open your presents.'

I ran to my presents, which were piled high next to my birthday cake. Just in time, I caught the top one as it wobbled over. I snatched it up. It was an inviting little parcel, and I opened it instantly.

Inside, lying on a soft velvety cushion, was a gorgeous ring, shaped like a delicate buttercup with a tiny ruby nestling in the middle. I put on the ring and went over to give Grandpa Joe a huge thank-you hug. Then Mum said I could open my other presents.

I was so busy looking at all my lovely things that I wasn't really listening to my grandparents chatting away, but I realised that they were talking about how brains work.

When my brothers, Brad and Lee, came in, I found myself saying: 'Oh, I wish I could get inside a brain!'

'Whatever for, silly?' said Brad. 'Nobody can do that!'

'But I would like to,' I replied, giving my ring a comforting little twist.

All of a sudden everything went black. I was spinning round and round, and then I landed with a bump.

When I opened my eyes I saw nothing but legs, brown wooden legs. Looking up I saw a huge birthday cake topped with gigantic candles. Brad and Lee loomed above me. I couldn't see their faces unless I lay on my back.

I HAD SHRUNK!

'Gosh!' I thought. 'Now I'm small enough to get inside a brain.' Brad's brain! What would be the best way in? I didn't like the idea of going through his nose or mouth... I would try his ears.

I darted from desk to table to sofa and finally reached Brad's foot. Luckily he was wearing his jeans and a woollen jumper, so I managed to scramble up his legs quite easily. And no one spotted me on my woolly climb – I was too small to be noticed. At last I reached the top. Puffing and panting, I stopped to catch my breath, perched on Brad's left shoulder. Then I made straight for his ear.

I peered inside. It was very dark. But I remembered I had put my new torch in my pocket. I switched it on and climbed into Brad's ear hole.

Twisting and turning round endless bends, I came at last to a closed door. I opened it. And there, on the other side, sat a fat, jolly man. He was tinkering with a tin box with a dial on the side. He did not stop working with his miniature spanners but he looked up.

'Hallo,' I said politely. 'My name's Kiki.'

'How do you do?' replied the fat man. 'I'm Mr Brainbox.'

'What are you doing?' I asked.

'Just seeing what's the matter with this ear. It's not working too well.'

'What are those levers marked *high* and *low*?' I asked.

'They help the ear hear high and low noises.' Mr Brainbox smiled at me. 'Would you like to see the rest of Brad's brain?'

'Oh, yes please,' I answered.

We walked along a long, dark passage until we came to a door marked *Ideas*. Pushing it open, we walked in.

This room was bigger than Mr Brainbox's. Along one side were strange-looking machines attached to various pipes and bottles. A red fizzy liquid bubbled away in them. Lined up on many shelves were bottles of coloured liquids. All were labelled.

Peering through his spectacles at us was a wizened old man. He wore brown fingerless gloves and he was holding a bottle of green liquid.

'What are you doing?' I asked

curiously. The old man jumped, dropping his glass bottle. It smashed and liquid seeped across the floor.

'Drat it – that was good homework dodge potion,' muttered the old man. He picked up a key pad, pressed a button and the roof opened. Two little robots carrying sponges and buckets jumped down and began to clear up the mess.

Mr Brainbox took me over to read the labels on the bottles.

'Excuses for being late.'

'Excuses for not doing homework.'

'Ideas for not feeling well at school.'

'Jokes to play on teachers.'

And there were lots more. But I wanted to explore, so I said goodbye to the little old man, and followed Mr Brainbox out of the *Ideas* room. Once more we were wandering down the long, dark passage. At last Mr Brainbox stopped and chose a room marked *Eyesight*. In the room were two men, one fat and one thin. Their skin was blue and they wore black clothes. Each was peering through a telescope.

'Of course,' I murmered. Brad's eyes. Brad has peculiar eyes – especially his pupils. One is fat, the other is thin!

'Do speak to them, my dear,' whispered Mr Brainbox.

'Hallo,' I said.

'Hallo,' they replied. 'Can't look at you now, not until he's gone to sleep.'

Now we were going through the door marked *Nerves*. I wished that Mr Brainbox hadn't opened that door.

We were surrounded by a horde of small round men. They were like hundreds of tiny bouncing balls and they had arms and legs sticking out all over the place.

A feather touched one of the nerves, and he yelled out.

'That couldn't have hurt you,' I

said scornfully.

'Oh, but it did. We nerves are so sensitive,' he explained.

'Yes, we are, we are,' chanted the other nerves.

They began to twitch up and down, and bounce against us. They had evil grins and clawing nails.

'Okay, okay,' I said, grabbing Mr Brainbox by the hand, and we rushed out slamming the door behind us.

'Oh, dear, oh dear, must you make such a noise?' said a very grumpy voice. And there, sitting in a deck chair, was a carbon copy of Brad's nose.

'Yes I must,' I said huffily. 'I'm not staying here to be insulted. How do I get out of here?'

'I couldn't tell you. All I do is sniff and smell. I haven't got a mind, you know.'

'Then why aren't you where you should be, sniffing and smelling?' I asked.

'I'm on holiday,' said the very stuffy nose.

'But what about Brad? What can he do without a nose?' I exclaimed.

'He can breathe. He can't smell, that's all. He's got a bit of a cold. You could try leaving by the mouth,' added the nose. 'Two doors down the corridor.'

'I think you've had enough adventures for now,' smiled Mr Brainbox. 'Off you go – and goodbye until next time we meet.'

'Goodbye Mr Brainbox. It was very kind of you to show me round.'

I followed the nose's directions, and found myself at a door through which I could feel a brisk draught. I opened it and saw ahead of me a long red pipe. I began to walk down it. Suddenly I was feeling very tired. I stopped outside a narrow red door, opened it slowly – and twisted my ring. Soon I was spinning round and round.

BUMP. I looked up, and saw Mum and Lee.

'Where am I? What happened?' I asked.

'Nothing, Kiki, you just fainted,' my mother replied. 'Too much excitement I expect.'

So I hadn't been inside Brad's brain and met Mr Brainbox and Mr Ideas....

Then Brad rushed in shouting, 'Mum, Mum, I've got a terrible cold. My nose is all blocked up. And my left ear has been tickling most DREADFULLY.'

And then I knew it really had happened. I won't tell anyone or they'll say I was dreaming. But I KNOW it happened. I hope you do too!

Keren Kristal

Football revenge

Henry hated football. He always had, and he reckoned that he always would. Luckily, no one at home expected him to like it or be good at it or even to play it. But at school all his friends seemed to think it was the best, the greatest, the most important thing in the world.

All playtime long a game of football, or even two or three, would rage up and down the playground. Anyone who didn't want to play got trampled, squashed, pushed or squeezed out of the way. The football tide flowed right up to the benches at one end of the playground and the wire fence at the other end. Even feet got trampled if you left them dangling down from the bench.

Henry was fed up. He had been trying to play transformers with Thomas and Amit and Chia when the football wave crashed over them and scattered everything.

'It's not fair,' he told Mum when he got home. 'We don't interfere with their football, but they never leave us in peace. And no one ever stops them, because football looks like a proper game.'

Mum made lots of suggestions. First she suggested that Henry try playing football. Henry groaned. 'I have tried, but I'm no good. No one wants me on their team.'

Then Mum suggested playing somewhere else. 'We're not allowed anywhere else,' said Henry. So she suggested asking the teacher.

'That's no good,' said Henry. 'Mr Taylor likes football too. He'd never stop it.'

Mum finally got tired of making suggestions. 'Well,' she said. 'You'll just have to think up something of your own.'

That night, when Henry was in bed, he did some thinking.

His younger brother Edward did some thinking, too.

'You could fight them, bash them all and tie them up in knots,' he said, and jumped up and down on the bed to demonstrate the fight, the bash and the knots.

'You could biff all the footballs into outer space.' He biffed some odd socks lying on the floor. One landed on top of the cupboard and dangled down just out of reach. The other never even made it into orbit, but drooped on to a LEGO model.

'You could cover the playground with Superglue so that they all stick down and can't kick any more.' He picked his feet up slowly, showing just how difficult it is to walk or kick in Superglue.

Henry said nothing. He was thinking.

That night, he dreamed of his football revenge.

Instead of a bedside light, Henry had a globe with a light inside. All night long the little globe shone and turned slowly round and round. In Henry's dream, the globe became a football. Not a dirty white plastic football that rolled about and was kicked by anyone who felt like it, but a multi-coloured ball that looked rather like a giant gobstopper. This ball wasn't for anyone to kick. This ball was Henry's, and he alone could control it.

Henry took his multi-coloured football into the playground. He spun it in his hands and then let it stop so that everyone could see that the colours

on it came from the different coloured countries on the globe. What nobody except Henry knew was that each colour produced a special effect. Touch red and a red-hot spark shot right through your body. Touch blue and it was like feeling ice – and blue was the most likely colour you could touch, as so much of the world is made up of sea. Yellow gave a jelly-like sensation. First toes, then legs, arms and finally your whole body began to feel soft, wobbly and so helpless that you would collapse in a heap. Green had the opposite effect. Anyone who touched green became still all over and creaky like a rusty robot.

Everyone gathered round Henry.

'Give us a turn.'

'Put it down. Put it down. Let *us* have a kick.'

'Spoil-sport! It's no use to you. You can't even play.'

Hands reached out to knock the ball to the ground, but Henry fended them off. He wanted to make quite sure that his revenge would work. He did want everyone to have a kick, but only when he was quite ready.

'Teams,' he said quietly. 'Make two teams.'

There was some shouting and shuffling, and then two teams were grouped together.

'You can be ref,' they said.

Henry smiled. He threw the ball high into the air.

'Game begins,' he shouted.

Everyone rushed for the ball. Elvin's toe was the first to connect.

'Ow, ow, ow!' he shrieked. 'The ball's burning hot!' He retired to the bench.

James had fallen into a heap in the middle of the playground.

'I can't stand,' he wailed. He had touched the yellow.

Sean was wobbling in a ridiculous position. One leg was stuck out as it had been when he had first kicked. He was trying hard to get it back to its proper place on the ground, but before he managed it the other players flowed over him and he was knocked over.

Soon there were no footballers left. They had all retired from the game in a huff. Some were rubbing toes or heads which felt as if they had been stung by a wasp or pricked by a pin. Some were trying to get some feeling back into frozen fingers and toes by wriggling them and rubbing them. Some felt still and some felt floppy. All of them were cross and confused.

Henry trotted out and collected the ball.

'Dud ball!' Tim shouted at him. 'There's something wrong with it.'

'No one wants to play football with a rotten ball like that. It bites!' said Alex.

'How come you can hold it OK?' Darren asked.

Henry said nothing. He took the ball and put it in his locker.

The middle of the playground was empty. There was no more football. Henry, Amit, Chia and Thomas played transformers. They could go wherever they liked. Lots of games which hadn't been played for ages started up in the big space in the middle of the playground.

Henry slept well. He slept so well that he overslept in the morning. Mum came in to wake him up.

'Come on,' she said. 'You can't hide there all day just because of the football.'

'I don't mind about football any more. Not at night, anyway,' Henry said.

And somehow, from that day on, Henry found that he didn't mind about football in the day so much either, because however bad it was he could always take his revenge at night.

Julia Eccleshare

The burglary – different viewpoints

Mother on the phone to her friend

'He didn't want to get up of course. I told him I'd heard a noise downstairs, but he just grunted and rolled over. Told me not to be so daft.

"I'm going," I told him. "If you won't go down then I will."

I put on my dressing gown and slipped out of the door. I stood for a moment and listened. Then I started down the stairs. I'd only taken a couple of steps when there was an almighty crash! It sounded as if my canteen of cutlery had been dropped on the floor. I froze. I just couldn't move.

He'd heard that of course. Couldn't fail to. Came out the bedroom white-faced, clutching his tennis racket. I nearly burst out laughing.

"Go on," he said, and pushed me from behind. We nearly had a full blown row right there on the stairs.

"You first," I hissed.

I'm sure whoever it was heard us. They were gone, of course, when we got there. Stuff was everywhere. The patio doors had been forced. He didn't seem to know what to do. I rang the police and then made us a cup of tea.'

Father in the train to work

'I heard this awful noise. She didn't hear it, she'd sleep through anything. Anyway, I woke her up and told her to stay in the bedroom while I went to investigate. I picked up the tennis racket – it was the only weapon I could think of – and started down the stairs.

I heard a noise behind me. She'd followed, of course.

"Go back," I hissed.

When I got downstairs, there was a chap in the living room. He was a nasty piece of work, tall and hefty. He'd unplugged our portable TV, and our cutlery and cut glasses were on the table. He didn't know what to do when he saw me. I yelled and waved my racket, then moved towards him, but he hurled the TV at me. Then he grabbed the cutlery and ran into the garden. I chased after him but he was out the back gate and away before I could get near him.

I went back in and phoned the police. Brenda was shaking so I sat her down and made us a cup of tea.'

Trish telling Karen on their way to school

'We were burgled last night. I didn't hear anything, but I woke up when the police arrived. I heard Dad telling the police what had happened. Mum kept quiet. Dad made himself out to be a bit of a hero. Mum didn't say anything.

There was a huge row when the police left. It seems that Dad wasn't brave after all. If it hadn't been for Mum, he'd have stayed in bed and done nothing.

Mum hasn't spoken to Dad this morning. Aren't grown-ups silly?'

Kevin tells his teacher at nursery school

'I slept through everything. I didn't see the burglar. I didn't hear the police. I didn't hear Mum and Dad arguing. But if I did hear anything I'd go downstairs and splurge him with my splatt gun.'

Brian Moses

The treasure hunt

My class is probably just like yours. We have big children, clever children, big heads and a couple of children who seem to get into more trouble than anyone else. During the last three weeks we have been studying pirates. My favourite is Blackbeard because my dad has a beard. He let me put ribbons in it so that he looked like the real Blackbeard going into battle. He looked more daft than deadly, even when he ran around our lounge shooting at all the ornaments with his pretend pistols!

As the half-term holiday came nearer Miss Harris, our teacher, told us we would end the topic with 'pirate day'. It sounded a bit boring; I expected Miss Harris to ask us all to dress up as pirates and sing songs. I could just imagine it, thirty Long John Silvers with stuffed parrots on their shoulders shouting, 'Ah, Jim-lad'. But, I was wrong, her idea was much better than that.

Before I tell you what happened I should introduce you to the main characters in this story. First there's Ajay; he is tall, clever and I think he's great. Next, there is Henry; he's very clever because his mum is a doctor. We call him brains because he looks and walks like Brains in *Thunderbirds*. Anne is horrible. She has long blond hair, the boys think she is beautiful, but she can be really nasty. Kenny is funny, but he doesn't mean to be. He is not the cleverest person on earth, he's more like mischief on legs. Pek came from Taiwan four years ago, he learned to speak English very quickly and is excellent at football. Pek lets the girls join in with his games, he's a lot fairer than most of the other boys. Last, but not least, there is Sarah. She is big, strong and loud. She is tough, rough and more than enough for most children in our school to handle. Oh yes, I nearly forgot, I'm Rachael. So now you know everyone, let's get started.

On 'pirate day' Miss Harris came into our classroom and explained that we were going to organise ourselves into groups and look for clues hidden around the school that would lead us to treasure. This sounded great fun and quick as a flash I grabbed Ajay and made sure I was in his group.

'Gerroff!' shouted Ajay. But I knew secretly he didn't really mind. Within three minutes we'd sorted ourselves into four groups of various sizes and Sarah stood on her own near Miss Harris. She put on her nobody-loves-me face.

'Nobody wants me, Miss,' whined Sarah. 'They say I'm too rough.'

'We'll have her, Miss,' shouted Kenny eagerly and then, 'OW!' as I kicked him under the table. Everyone knows Sarah fancies Ajay; the last thing I want is to have Sarah in my group.

'Thank you, Kenny,' said Miss Harris. 'Now Sarah, be a co-operative girl and don't dominate the group too much.' Sarah smiled sweetly, but none of us were fooled. Miss Harris then went on to explain that we would be given a clue which would help us to locate other clues. The first group to reach the end of the trail and discover the treasure was the winner. Miss Harris didn't tell us what the treasure was, she simply said it would be items that were 'valuable to us'.

There were six people in my group: Ajay, Sarah, Kenny, Helen, Pek and myself. Ajay was voted our leader. He's good at being in charge because he listens to what everyone says and uses all our ideas, not just his own. The only one who didn't vote for Ajay was Sarah. She wanted to be captain herself, surprise, surprise.

'You can't be captain, you're a girl!' said Kenny. As far as Kenny is concerned all pirates were men, so all captains must be men too. He's never heard of the pirates Anne Bonny and Mary Read!

'Sarah can be my second in command,' said Ajay. That pleased Sarah but made me feel jealous.

Kenny ran to Miss Harris and returned with a small piece of paper. Ajay took charge of the clue and read it to us.

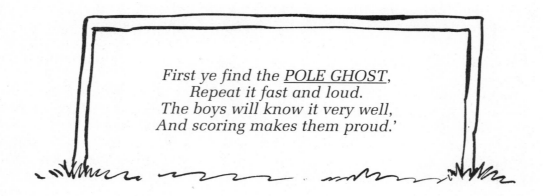

First ye find the <u>POLE GHOST</u>,
Repeat it fast and loud.
The boys will know it very well,
And scoring makes them proud.'

We looked at each other completely baffled.

'What's a pole ghost?' asked Kenny. 'Our school is too new to have a ghost, only old buildings have ghosts.'

'Why will *boys* know it very well?' I asked. 'Why not girls?'

'What do boys do more than girls?' Ajay asked.

'Get dirty!' said Kenny.

'Argue!' said Sarah, which is a bit rich as she argues more than anyone in school.

'Play football!' said Helen

'Have girlfriends,' suggested Pek.

'What about repeating pole ghost quickly?' I said. 'Pole ghost is underlined in the clue, and it says "repeat it fast and loud".'

So we did. (You could try it too.) Kenny had a go, it went like this...

'Pole ghost, pole ghost, pole ghost, pole ghost, goal post, GOAL POST!'

'GOAL POST!' we all screamed at the top of our voices, and then 'SSHHHHHH!' as we looked around to see all the other groups staring at us. Then suddenly everyone dived for the door in an attempt to be first out on to the football pitch and first to the goal posts!

Ajay, Helen, Kenny, Pek and I made it through the door first, leaving Sarah to close it and hold on to the handle to prevent the rest of the class from following us. By the time the rest of the class had forced it open, Kenny and I had reached one goal post and Ajay, Helen and Pek had reached the other. Kenny found a small piece of paper near the base of one post.

'Found it !' he bellowed, and then stuffed the paper into his mouth as the rest of our class ran to where we were standing. Sarah jogged up behind the throng of angry children.

'Where's the treasure?' demanded Anne.

'There's no treasure yet,' said Ajay, 'just a note. We were here first so we'll read it first.'

'Only because Sarah stopped us getting out of the classroom!' exploded Anne.

'The door was stuck. I was trying to open it for you,' grinned Sarah, doing her imitation of a crocodile.

'Give me the note please, Kenny,' said Ajay.

Kenny pulled the note from his mouth and everyone screwed up their faces in disgust.

'Why did you do that, Kenny?' asked Ajay patiently.

'It's top secret!' said Kenny. 'Spies do it on the telly. When they're captured the spies always swallow the secret code.'

Kenny handed the soggy piece of paper to Ajay. He read the note to himself and then to the eager crowd.

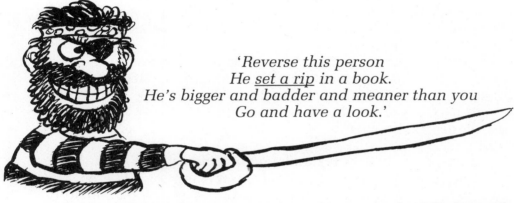

'*Reverse this person*
He <u>*set a rip*</u> *in a book.*
He's bigger and badder and meaner than you
Go and have a look.'

While Sarah spied on Henry's group, my group huddled together, like a rugby team at half time.

'Any ideas?' asked Ajay.

'Nope!' said Kenny. Well, at least he's honest.

'It's a man or boy we're looking for because it says "he" in the clue,' said Helen.

'It could be Mr Wilkins, the caretaker,' suggested Pek.

'The clue says he's big, bad and mean. But Mr Wilkins is shorter than some of the children in Year 3 and he's really kind and helpful too,' said Ajay.

At that moment Sarah ran over to join us like a charging rhino and began talking excitedly.

'Henry's team think the clue is a hologram – you know, where the letters of a word are jumbled up to make another word. Henry's really clever, he must be right!'

'You mean *anagram*, not *hologram*,' said Ajay. 'Well done, Sarah, good spying.' Sarah beamed. Pek wrote out all the letters from 'set a rip' in his notebook and we all thought as hard as we could. Kenny's eyes crossed and uncrossed with the effort.

'REST!' shouted Kenny. 'You can make 'rest' from the letters!'

'Good one,' said Ajay. 'but you have to use all the letters, you've only used four.'

'SEA TRIP!' shouted Pek. 'That uses all the letters.'

Ajay lowered his voice. 'The clue says "reverse this person", look at the letters and spell the words "set a rip" backwards.'

'PIRATES,' I whispered.

'Well done, Rachael,' said Pek.

Now we knew what the anagram might be, we looked back at the clue.

'It says "set a rip in a book". It must be a pirate in a book,' suggested Helen.

'A big, bad, mean one,' said Kenny. 'The pirate must be Blackbeard, he was the biggest and baddest of them all.'

Well, where were we going to find a book on Blackbeard? In the library of course! We ran towards the school building and as we passed Henry's group Sarah shouted, 'It's DUSTBINS! The clue says DUSTBINS!' We ran on while the rest of our class raced to the kitchen where the dustbins were kept. As we disappeared inside we heard the cook screaming at the class as they tipped the contents of three dustbins on to the ground.

Once in the library, it didn't take long to find the right encyclopaedia. As we flicked through the first volume to find BL... we saw a map tucked between Blackbeard and Blackpool. It was a plan of our classroom with a large red cross marked in one corner.

We quickly made our way to the classroom. As we passed the Head's office, the rest of our class were just entering his room in silence and with faces as long as the day before your birthday.

'Getting told off?' asked Sarah

'Of course we are!' sulked Anne. 'It's your fault, you told us the clue was in the dustbins!'

'Sorry,' said Sarah, 'I never was much good at spelling.' We left the rest of our class in the Head's office and walked to our classroom. There was no need to hurry now, the Head would drone on for ages about responsibility and appropriate behaviour and all the other things Heads say.

The map took us to the stock cupboard in one corner of the room. Inside were lots of shelves loaded with exercise books, tins of paint powder, balls of string and hundreds of other things you will only ever find in a teacher's cupboard. One shelf, however, was completely clear except for a biscuit tin. Ajay lifted it down.

'What do you think it will be? asked Pek.

'Treasure! Gold, silver and diamonds,' said Kenny with eyes as bright as milk-bottle tops.

'I doubt it!' said Ajay. 'Miss Harris said it would be things that we value. Let's open it and find out'

Kenny tipped it upside down spilling everything over the table top. We were very pleased with our 'treasure' though. There were sweets, new pencils with 'Treasure Hunter' written on them, some badges with pirates on the front and, best of all, enough book tokens to buy pirate books for the class library.

We visited the local bookshop after school and spent an hour choosing the pirate books on behalf of our class. We have a list of people waiting to read them. My group was allowed to choose first as we were the champion treasure hunters!

Ian Purnell

Grandad's teeth

I thought that Grandad was just an ordinary old man
Until he came to spend a holiday with us.
Early one morning before anyone else was awake
I crept into his bedroom
To see if he wanted to play war;
War games with Grandad are always fun
Because he always lets me win,
But he was snoring,
Only his face bristling with grey grass
And with more cracks in it than dried mud
Peeked open-mouthed above the bedclothes.
He looked so old and tired that I decided
Our war could wait until after breakfast.
I was just about to leave
When I noticed something different about Grandad's face:
His cheeks were hollow and his lips
Had all but disappeared.
I was just about to shout Mum
To tell her that Grandad was ill
When I noticed his teeth
In a glass of water
On a table
By his bed;
They were smiling at me
So I knew that Grandad must be all right.
Later, when he came down to breakfast
The same teeth smiled at me again
But this time they were back in Grandad's mouth.
Now, whenever he comes to stay
I wait until he's fast asleep
Then I sneak in and search his room
to see what other parts of his body
Grandad's taken off and hidden.

Frank Flynn

Remember, remember...

A smack bottom, a lollipop tree, a pike's teeth...?
What will you most remember about being small?

One of my children, who is now grown-up, particularly remembers receiving just one smack on her bottom! Not a very exciting thing to remember, you would think – I had certainly forgotten about giving it to her!

The smack was for lying: she said she had cleaned her teeth, then I found her toothbrush, quite dry, just afterwards! I don't think the smack can have done much good at the time, as she says that after that she just used to make sure she dipped her brush under the tap to wet it – even if she *didn't* clean her teeth! On the other hand, perhaps it did do some good, as she's now a very enthusiastic teeth-cleaner, and often brushes them three times a day!

Her brother and sister both remember waking up on one birthday to find a real lollipop tree outside their window! (We had carefully fastened all the lollipops to our baby willow tree the night before.)

Much later, just before she left school, my eldest daughter wrote about something else she remembered: the mealtime when her brother flicked a prune stone across the dinner table – while their dad was talking about good manners!

I wonder if people often only remember the 'naughty bits'? One friend told me about hiding in a cupboard to avoid washing up; others recall 'finding' presents which were supposed to be hidden away for Christmas! Certainly one or two of my memories are to do with trouble, like yelling at the school gate to go home on my first day at school, or once forgetting to put the brake on my baby sister's pushchair when it was on a slope... luckily there was someone around to catch it!

I think people often remember things that 'weren't fair', too. When I was about six years old I picked a beautiful bunch of may-blossom to take to my mother. This caused trouble: it was supposed to be unlucky to have may-blossom in the house. I never found out why, but it had to go!

What would be your most *scary* memory? One of mine would be pike's teeth! I was in a small, borrowed rowing boat with my father, floating along a quiet Lincolnshire dyke, when we saw the pike – and his teeth!

'What do they eat?' I asked my father. We were very close to the fish; he had lifted the oars out of the water so that it wouldn't be disturbed. 'Oh, they'll eat anything,' he replied quietly. My eyes didn't move from those teeth as we drifted closer. After a minute or two's hesitation I fearfully asked, 'Even this rowing boat?'

'Oh, even that!' smiled my father. It was a long time before I went rowing again.

Memories! Happy or sad, troublesome, frightening, embarrassing or proud. I wonder what kind of memories *yours* will be a few years from now?

Judith Nicholls

ON THE MOVE

I don't like this house!

One very sad day Charlotte and her family moved house. 'I don't like this house,' said Charlotte.

'Nonsense!' said her mother. 'It's in a street that's quiet and peaceful.'

Charlotte looked out of the window. She looked up the street and down the street. She looked across and beyond, as far as her eyes could see. Where were all the cars and bicycles? Where were all the busy people? Where were all the skipping children?

There were none to be seen. Outside was as quiet as a sleeping lion.

'I don't like this house,' said Charlotte.

'Nonsense!' said her mother, 'It's got lovely big rooms!'

Charlotte went to explore. She went up the stairs and down the stairs. She went through the doors and round the walls. She peered into the attic and squinted down into the cellar. Where were all the cosy corners? Where were all the crooked walls? Where were all the slanting roofs?

There were none to be seen. All through this house were high, high, ceilings, and walls so long they'd never run out. Inside was vast and echoey as a singing whale.

'I don't like this house,' said Charlotte.

'Nonsense!' said her mother. 'It's got lots and lots of cupboard space.'

Charlotte opened the cupboards. She opened one under the stairs, but it was empty. She opened two in the kitchen, but there was nothing inside. She opened three in the bedroom, but nothing fell out. Where were all the brooms and buckets? Where were all the pots and pans? Where were the friendly books and the dog-eared teddies?

There were none to be seen. The cupboards were as empty as a hungry bear's cave.

'I don't like this house,' said Charlotte.

'Nonsense!' said her mother. 'It's got more space.'

So Charlotte went back to look at the spaces. She marched through the living room and into the hall. She trotted up the stairs and along the landing. She paced through the bedrooms and shuffled in the bathroom. Where were all the nooks and crannies? Where were all the piled up corners? Where were all her favourite places?

There were none to be seen. The space was as huge and unfriendly as a biting tiger.

'I don't like this house,' said Charlotte.

'Nonsense!' said her mother. 'It will be much better for the animals.'

So Charlotte went tracking. She looked for Pip's lead, but it wasn't on the hook. She searched for Fluff's basket, but it wasn't by the window. She tried rummaging for Henry's treadwheel, but there was nowhere to rummage. Where were the barks and leaps and licks? Where were the mews and purrs and stretches? Where the squeaks and scrabbles and scratches?

There were none to be found. Everywhere was as still as a sleeping crocodile.

'I don't like this house,' said Charlotte.

'Nonsense!' said her mother. 'It's got a beautiful back garden. Why don't you go outside and see?'

So Charlotte did. On the slabs where Jamie's pram should be, there was a strawberry tub, with great, fat, juicy strawberries tumbling all over it. Where she expected a rusty old swing to be creaking to and fro, there stood an apple tree, covered with small green apples.

Where she thought she would find a falling-down shed and a heap of dusty bricks, there was a mass of canes spilling with ripe, red tomatoes.

And right in the corner, instead of an overgrown hedge with its prickles and tangles waiting to catch her, there was a forest of bushes oozing with plump raspberries, just begging to be picked. Well!

Charlotte began to pick the raspberries. She collected some early windfall apples from the lawn. She gathered tomatoes for tea. She pulled fat strawberries from the tub and laid them carefully in rows to count. And while she was picking and collecting and gathering and pulling, she munched and she crunched and she dribbled the juice down her chin, and she had such fun that she didn't hear the removal van arrive.

Then there was a great humping of furniture, and an excited scurrying and sniffing of cats and dogs and hamsters, and a tremendous welcoming of teddies and toys and books and pots and pans and brooms and prams and babies and dads and everything else. But Charlotte was so busy with her harvesting that she missed it all.

At last, when all her fruit was safely gathered for tea, Charlotte went inside. Then she looked around in astonishment. 'I like this house,' she said happily. 'It's just like home!'

Irene Yates

Round the world with a tyre

When I was not quite five, I lived near a dump. This was a long time ago, and there weren't half the cars on the road that there are now. But on the dump, which was where people threw things away, there were always hundreds of tyres.

My friend, Harry Carter, and I loved that dump. We never knew what we'd find. There'd be marvellous tins and beautiful battered boxes. There'd be broken chairs, and tables with only three legs. And there'd be tyres. Every time we went there, we admired the tins and boxes. We tried to make the three-legged tables stand up, which they wouldn't. Then we'd choose a tyre and bowl it away. The bigger the better. I can't remember Harry's face now. That's because it was usually hidden behind the tyre he was bowling down the street.

Sometimes we'd meet another boy bowling *his* tyre in the opposite direction. And because we were smaller than our tyres, they'd collide and fall over with a great hollow rubbery clunk. And there we'd stand, making angry faces at each other.

'You knocked my tyre over!'

'No, I didn't! *You* knocked *my* tyre over!'

It could lead to battle.

It must have been awkward in those days for any grown-ups who made the mistake of being around.

The streets were full of boys bowling enormous tyres! Sometimes, if there was a bit of a slope, we'd lose control. The tyres would roll faster than we could follow them, and if they headed for some unlucky adult, then we'd either have to run after them… or just run away.

When the day was over, and I had to go in to bed, I always had the problem of how best to hide my tyre. It had two enemies. One was the boy next door, who wanted it for himself. If I hid it under the hedge at the back of the garden, and my mum called me in at six, and his mum called him in at a quarter past six, he had a quarter of an hour to hunt around and find it. Then he'd take it next door and hide it under *his* hedge, and next morning there'd be another battle.

'That's *my* tyre!'

'Prove it!'

I never could. If I said it was a tyre off a motorbike, he'd say his was off a motorbike too. If I said mine was an extra-big one with DUNLOP written on it, he'd say his was an extra-big one with DUNLOP written on it.

Then I'd lost my tyre.

Its other enemy was my dad or my mum. *He'd* told me hundreds of times that he didn't want to find dirty old tyres under his back hedge. *She'd* said she was tired of washing the dirt off my hands after I'd spent all day bowling those filthy tyres all over the street. And Mrs Grumbler next door had complained that my tyre had only just missed her.

Dirty tyres? Terrible filthy tyres? What a way to talk about tyres! And Mrs Grumbler ought to have told my mum how *clever* I was to miss her. She ought to have said, 'Your lad knows how to control a tyre. You must be proud of him. I've been watching, and he's the best of the lot.'

So sometimes I was happy, because I had this particularly fine tyre and it was safely hidden and I could lie in bed and think about bowling it up and down the street all the next day. And sometimes I was miserable, because my tyre had gone and my mum said I wasn't to go back to the dump and get another one.

'No dump today,' she'd say. She'd made me look my best, ready for a visit to Aunty Hilda that afternoon; and look at my face already! 'You'd think it had never known what it was to be washed!' I was probably the dirtiest boy there'd ever been in the whole world. 'Heaven knows what Aunty Hilda will think!'

But I knew what Aunty Hilda would think. That was because she always said it.

'I give up! Boys are the limit! I think they'd *eat* dirt if you served it up for dinner!'

If my mum and my aunts had their way, I'd spend my whole life in the bathroom. When one of them was tired of washing me, than another would come and take over.

But I remember one day when all was well. All was wonderfully well!

Harry and I had two of the best tyres we'd ever found on the dump. He had DUNLOP written on his, and on mine I had a pair of wings. It was like an angel without a head. The wings seemed to make this tyre bowl along faster than any I'd ever had before. It was the greatest tyre ever, and of course it was in the hands of the greatest-ever bowler of tyres!

Harry and I set off at a spanking pace in the direction of Africa.

Well, I thought Africa probably wasn't very far beyond the church at the bottom of the road. I'd gone past it once or twice with my dad, but only a step or two. The other way was the dump, and that was more or less the end of the world in that direction. To the left there was a road we weren't allowed go down. To the right there was a steam laundry. There were great wheels inside and outside the building, and immense leather straps ran round the wheels. The laundry shook with the movement of those straps. There was a funnel on the roof that puffed out steam. It was as if the laundry was gasping for breath. It smelt too, of... laundry, and soap, and being clean. Sometimes I'd think Mum and Aunty Hilda might take me to the laundry and simply leave me there, to be everlastingly scrubbed and hung up to dry and ironed.

So there we were, Harry and I, that good day, setting off towards Africa. That is, as we thought, down the road to the church. Once there, we'd go twice round the war memorial, and then back home. Mission completed.

And that's where the good day became a bad day.

At some point, unable to see over our tyres, we went wrong. Instead of stopping short at Africa, we headed for the North Pole. That's to say, as I know now, we turned towards the laundry. But we didn't reach it. If we had, we'd have heard all that puffing and known where we were. Instead, we must somehow have turned into a side road.

The tyres were moving beautifully.

It was one of those afternoons that go on for ever. We'd never been better than this at tyre bowling. It was definitely the best afternoon of our lives.

But after a time I wondered what had happened to the church.

Harry must have wondered that, too. Because suddenly – he was ahead of me – his tyre began to tremble, and then slowly it fell sideways and then lay flat on the pavement. And I stopped bowling too, and *my* tyre trembled and fell flat on the pavement. And now we could see we weren't anywhere near the church. We weren't even in Africa. We weren't at the North Pole. If there was some terrible name for where we were, it must be Australia. I'd heard of Australia, and it was about as far from home as you could get.

Harry said, 'Where are we?'

Well, the houses Harry and I lived in were small and all alike. The houses we were looking at now were big and all different. I remember one house had a path leading to a front door that had glass over it. You walked up to the front door under glass! I'd never seen anything like it! Our own houses had simple short paths, and simple front doors. Some of the front doors here had great pillars, and little roofs of their own. All *our* houses were known by numbers. I lived in number 232. These houses had names. There wasn't a number to be seen.

Where were we?

Harry said, 'What shall we do?'

Mum had said if I was ever lost to say I came from 232 East Barnet Road. But who was I to say this to? There was nobody to be seen.

In *our* streets, there were always kids, and always quite a few grown-ups. In *this* street, there was nobody.

Australia was empty and silent.

I said, 'Let's go back the way we came!'

It was the only idea I had. Perhaps, if you'd gone wrong, the thing to do was to turn round and... do what you'd done before, but backwards.

So Harry and I turned and picked up our tyres and began bowling back the way we'd come. Except, of course, that we weren't at all sure *which* way we'd come.

I suppose it took ten minutes or so, that return journey. I remember it taking for ever. We just bowled along blindly. This time I was in the lead, and I didn't dare to think of where I was going. I just went. The pavements flew past, grey, grey, grey. All the pavements were the same. Wherever I looked, there was nothing I recognised.

And then...

I still remember the joy of it. To think that, after all, I'd see Mum again. And Dad. I'd have my tea, after all. I was even, at that moment, glad to think I'd see Aunty Hilda again.

At that moment, I WAS GLAD!

Because, to my left, I heard a

puffing. I heard the flapping sound the great belts made. I smelt the smell of great cleanliness. I knew where we were.

We'd found the laundry....

It wasn't long after that when I went to school for the first time and Miss Stout, our teacher, told us about the world. The world was very big, she said. It was very much bigger than East Barnet. And it was round. There was a man called Christopher Columbus who'd bowled his tyre... no, he'd sailed his ship across the huge sea, believing the world was round and he was safe. Lots of people at the time thought that Christopher Columbus would sail off the edge of it and go spinning to his death in space.

But they were wrong, and Christopher Colombus was right. He proved the world was round.

I thought, and I said to Harry, that Christopher Columbus might have been the first to prove it, but Harry and I hadn't been far behind. That afternoon when we couldn't find the church, we'd proved the world was round.

Well, obviously, Harry and I had been round it.

Edward Blishen

That's really flying!

If you think flying in an airliner is exciting you should try taking a ride in a Tiger Moth, an aircraft that's fifty years old. We've got a photograph of me sitting in the front cockpit, a Biggles look alike, with helmet, goggles, and warm flying jacket.

The flight was a birthday present, a million times better than the usual book tokens. It happened because I'd just finished building a model Tiger Moth. This had been tricky because it's a biplane. There are two sets of wings, one above and one below the fuselage and bits of wire criss-cross between them. That wire was a real pain to get right.

Then my mum saw an advertisement in our local paper: 'THE ULTIMATE GIFT. A TEN-MINUTE FLIGHT IN A VINTAGE TIGER MOTH.'

'What's ultimate?' I asked. It meant the best gift anyone could have. Anyone who wanted it that is. I definitely wanted it!

'And what's vintage?'

Vintage meant it was old, special and valuable.

The aircraft was parked outside the hangar. It was silver with RAF roundels and a yellow stripe on the fuselage and wings, just like my model. I'd taken my colour scheme from the picture on the box.

First the pilot and I walked round the outside. We were checking it hadn't been damaged since its last flight. The wings and fuselage weren't metal, they were 'fabric'. That's cloth fastened on to the aircraft's wooden frame, then painted with varnish to make it strong.

We were looking for holes and hoping not to find any. Mice get into old aeroplanes and start nesting and nibbling the fabric.

Because there are no brakes on a Tiger Moth the wheels have chocks put

in front of them so that when the engine is started the aircraft doesn't jump forward. Chocks are small triangular wooden wedges. The plane flies from grassy fields so stopping without brakes isn't the problem it would be on a concrete runway. There's also a metal spoon-shaped skid instead of a tail wheel. The skid drags along the ground and helps slow the aircraft down.

I dressed in the jacket, helmet and goggles. The helmet had a face mask attached like you see in Second World War flying films. The mask had a small microphone inside and there were earphones in the helmet so we could carry on a conversation between the two cockpits.

I stepped up on to a specially strengthened bit of the wing and climbed into the front cockpit. Someone strapped me in; there was a shoulder harness and a lap strap. Good idea since the cockpit isn't closed in.

The pilot explained the instruments. There weren't many. A compass for direction, an altimeter for height, a rev counter for engine speed, an air speed indicator to show the aircraft's speed through the air (not speed over the ground, that depends on the wind's strength and its direction). There was also a 'turn and slip indicator' so you can tell whether you're turning or flying level when you don't have a horizon because you're in cloud.

The pilot asked me to be careful not to rest my feet on the rudder pedals, not to grab the control stick or touch the throttle lever. There are controls in both cockpits because the Tiger Moth was built as a training aircraft. Unfortunately I wasn't going to get a flying lesson that day! Pity.

The pilot climbed into the back cockpit. While he was getting strapped in, another man came to swing the propeller. 'Contact,' called the pilot. The man pulled the propeller blade downwards and moved back swiftly. The engine roared into life.

We sat there for a few minutes while the engine warmed up and we got cold in the air rushing backwards from the spinning prop. The pilot opened the throttle and ran the engine fast for a few seconds, checking it. Then he throttled back again calling 'Chocks away'.

We bumped along the grass to the start of the runway. 'Ready?' shouted the pilot.

'Ready,' I shouted back. Even with the microphones we had to shout to be heard above the engine. I gave a 'thumbs up'. I'd seen that in the films.

With full power we charged along the runway. The pilot pushed the control stick fowards so that the tail came up off the ground. We went even faster without the drag from the tail skid. One second we were bumping along the grass at sixty miles an hour, the next we were airborne.

I saw the hedge at the end of the field and ducked. We cleared it easily. I stuck out my arm to wave to Mum, but the wind was so strong it was like pulling your arm through a barrel of treacle. I put my head over the side to look down, but the little bit of my face that wasn't covered by helmet, mask and goggles got whipped by the wind. It was cold up here.

We flew a gentle turn to the left. The top and bottom wings tilted downwards and I looked down through the criss-cross of wires.

'How high are we?' I called.

'One thousand feet. Look at your altimeter. The little hand shows the thousands of feet, the big hand the hundreds.'

It was like one o'clock on a clock.

'Your house is close by, we'll go and look at it,' the pilot said. I peered down. There was a row of identical houses, except that one had a big white cross on the back lawn. And people waving. The pilot circled. I could see a dog chasing round and round, the way *our* daft dog does whenever she hears an aircraft. Then I twigged. It *was* our house! I tried to wave. The pilot waggled the wings.

'Going back now,' he shouted. 'Can you see the airfield?' He pointed over to the left. 'It's in your nine o'clock position.'

I scanned the horizon on the port side (that's the left) and saw a large green space with a line of markers down the middle. That was it.

The pilot circled overhead keeping a good lookout for other aircraft. Tiger Moths don't have radios so they can't call up the control tower for landing instructions. He throttled back and we started to lose height. The air became warmer as we descended. We circled the airfield in a big curve until we were lined up with the runway. With the engine throttled back it was much quieter and there were ghostly whiny swishing noises made by the wind rushing over the aircraft's surfaces.

The wheels touched down. We were still going fast. I was getting worried about the hedge again. Then the tail dropped gently on to the grass and we rolled to a stop.

I tried to undo my safety harness and climb out but my fingers were stiff with cold and I couldn't feel my feet. And I hadn't even noticed! Funny the way you don't notice discomfort when you're enjoying yourself.

Pauline Young

The rescue

'Fresh laver bread for tea,' announced Aunty Mabel as she cleared up the breakfast dishes. It was the first day of the summer holidays, and Katy was paying her first grown-up visit without her mum and dad to her Aunt Mabel, who lived in the seaside village of Mumbles.

'Ooh great, I love fresh bread!' replied Katy. Her Aunty and her cousin smiled.

'Oh, we'll have to see if you like

this sort,' said her Aunty. 'You can go with Sarah and collect some this morning.'

Katy held her big cousin's hand as they set off down the road towards the shops.

Katy noticed the orange plastic bucket that her cousin was carrying.

'What have you got that for?'

'To put the laver bread in,' replied Sarah.

'My mum uses a proper shopping basket,' Katy sniffed. She suddenly caught sight of the bread shop across the road. The window was filled with a delicious display of mouth-watering cakes and pastries. Katy licked her lips and tried to decide which item was the laver bread.

'Come on slow-coach!' Sarah pulled her arm and gently led her along the road that led to the sea-shore.

'But you've passed the bread shop,' wailed Katy.

'I know,' replied Sarah, 'but we're not going there.'

'Oh! Do you have to get laver bread from a special shop then?' enquired Katy, as the bakery window passed out of sight.

'You don't get it from a shop,' explained her cousin.

'My mum always gets our bread from a proper shop!' declared Katy. 'A proper bakery!'

'I bet they don't sell laver bread though,' laughed Sarah.

By now the two children had reached the sea-wall and ahead of them through the early morning mist they could see the Mumbles Lifeboat Station, with its slipway dipping down into the water.

'See the lifeboat station,' Sarah pointed. 'Just before Christmas I saw the lifeboat being launched. There was a tremendous bang, and this rocket shot up over the village and exploded. It was like Bonfire Night. That's the signal for the lifeboat-men to get to the lifeboat as fast as they can. Mum and I rushed down there just in time to see the boat hit the water. They saved six men from a tanker that had broken down in rough seas.'

Katy gazed beyond the lifeboat station to a rocky hill looming out of the mist that seemed to stick out into the sea. Perched on top of it, like a giant stick of seaside rock, was the M u m b l e s Lighthouse. The light flashed into her eyes.

'Why doesn't the light stay on all the time?' Katy asked. 'Is its battery running down?'

Sarah grinned at her cousin. 'It's on all the time,' she explained. 'But the light turns round so that it flashes in all directions. That way people out to sea can see it. Come on, you'll soon get a closer look at it, 'cos that's where we're going.'

They soon came to the steps leading down to the beach. Katy picked her way carefully between piles of fronded brown seaweed and the sandy casts of the lug worms. At last they reached the rocky island on which stood the lighthouse.

'This looks just right,' announced

Sarah. Katy turned to see her cousin filling the plastic bucket with large handfuls of seaweed.

'What are you doing that for?' she asked.

'This is it! This is what we came for! Our tea!' said Sarah.

She dropped another glistening dollop into the bucket. 'This is laver bread.'

'Laver bread!' shrieked Katy. 'That's not bread, that's SEAWEED – yuck!'

Sarah scooped a final handful and threw it into the bucket with a satisfying squelch.

Katy gazed wide eyed at her cousin.

'You've got to be joking! I'm not eating that!'

'Please yourself,' laughed Sarah, 'but you'll be missing a treat!'

Katy shuddered and rambled off to examine one of the hundreds of tiny rock pools scattered around the bottom of the island. She got down on her knees and peered into a likely looking one. Below the water was a whole new world, no bigger than the hand-basin in the bathroom. Tiny white barnicles encrusted the rocks, looking like fairy-tale castles, or the teeth of some sea monster, and scuttling for cover under a pebble was a baby crab, desperately trying to collapse its legs so the great giant outside wouldn't notice it.

Sarah joined her and they became completely absorbed in the little rock pool world, rolling pebbles into it, and poking lumps of seaweed with sticks. Suddenly Katy felt a damp

sort of feeling spreading around her knees. Looking down she saw sea water flooding round her legs.

'Oh no!' Sarah leapt to her feet. The tide had come in and between the lighthouse island and the safety of the sea wall was an ever-deepening channel of water.

'We can still paddle across if we're quick,' suggested Katy brightly.

Sarah shook her head. 'Not likely. Look how fast the tide's coming in!'

Katy burst into tears.

'Oh don't cry!' Sarah gazed around frantically. There was a row of fishermen sitting on the end of the pier. 'Come on. Wave for help!'

The children waved frantically. The fishermen were all too busy tending to their fishing lines, but after a while one man looked across in their direction. Katy and Sarah jumped up and down.

'Help, oh help!'

The fisherman took his pipe out of his mouth and waved cheerfully back at them.

'Oh, it's no use,' sighed Sarah. 'We can't stay here until the tide goes out again. My mum will be worried sick. We'll have to climb up to the lighthouse and ask for help.'

They both looked up at the rocky slope that led to the lighthouse. Katy began to take her crying seriously and let out a high pitched wail.

'Ssshh!' hissed Sarah. Katy gulped and switched off her home-made siren for a moment. In the distance they could hear a strange buzzing sound, 'brrrrrrrrrrrrrrrrr'.

'Listen,' whispered Katy.

'Brrrrrrrrrrrrrrrr...oooom.'

From around the black, iron legs of the pier shot a bright orange dinghy with the letters RNLI painted on the side. Two men wearing yellow life-jackets sat next to the outboard motor which sent the little craft skimming over the waves and towards the two girls. Within a matter of moments Katy and Sarah, together with their precious bucket of seaweed, were speeding past the pier towards the lifeboat station. As they passed the pier this time, the fishermen waved.

'Shame on you, Sarah Evans,' scolded the lifeboat-man, waving his finger under her nose. 'Lived here all your life, and you forgot about the tide! You wouldn't believe the number of people we have to rescue off the lighthouse during the summer.' He handed the bucket over, 'So remember, next time you're after laver bread, keep an eye on the tide!'

Katy and her cousin thanked the crew of the lifeboat, and even offered them some seaweed. The lifeboat-men politely refused the offer. 'I'll be for it when we get home,' sighed Sarah. 'Fancy forgetting the tide!'

Half an hour later, after a sharp telling-off from Aunt Mabel, the two girls were seated at the kitchen table watching a pile of seaweed sizzling in the frying pan. Aunty Mabel spooned a little on to Katy's plate. She looked at her cousin, and fearfully lifted a forkful to her mouth. She closed her eyes, screwed up her nose, and popped it into her mouth. Slowly a delighted grin spread across her face.

Merlin Price

Rebecca's world

Rebecca lived in a big house in the country. At least it seemed like a big house to her, but then she was quite small, so perhaps it wasn't all that large.

It was the eleventh day of the school holidays and she was bored. Bored. Bored. Bored.

She had mooned and moped around the house all day, getting under everybody's feet, until finally her mother said in a tense, tight voice: 'Go upstairs and play in your room.'

Rebecca walked mournfully along the landing. She closed her eyes and stretched her arms out in front of her, wondering how far she could go before she ran into something.

There was a muffled crash. Rebecca opened one eye and saw that she had knocked over a vase of flowers from the window-sill. It had broken and the water was soaking into the carpet.

'It's not fair,' she thought miserably. 'I bet I'll get blamed for that.'

She closed her eyes again and moved on blindly, walking over the flowers. This time she managed to go quite a long way without touching anything. She took a sneaky peep and found she was standing outside the closed door of her father's study.

She knocked. There was no answer.

She opened the door and went in. There was a huge window at one end of the room. Standing alongside it was her father's brand new astral telescope. Rebecca had been strictly told that on no account was she to touch it.

So she went across and touched it.

The telescope swung easily under her hand and tilted upwards at the already darkening sky.

Rebecca stared out through the window. There was only one star to be seen. It was a very long way off, blue, white and twinkling.

'I bet the people who live on that star aren't bored,' she thought. 'I bet they're always doing exciting things and having adventures.'

She wondered if she would be able to see what they were doing if she looked through the telescope. She put her eye close to the lens thing that you look into and turned the knob to focus it – the way she had seen her father do.

Suddenly there was the star looking bigger and brighter, although still far away. There was no sign of any people. As she stared, Rebecca wondered more and more about things that happened on the star. She wished that she could go there and find out. Just a little visit. Not for long.

Then a very strange thing occurred. Rebecca had the oddest feeling that somebody on the star was looking at her. She couldn't say why. It was just a feeling. But if they were, and were looking at her through the wide end of her father's telescope, then she would appear to be very tiny. Rebecca knew that if you look down the wrong end of a telescope everything seems much smaller.

And then another peculiar thing happened. Rebecca began to *feel* smaller. And as she did, the star appeared to become larger. It became so large that it filled the whole telescope. The glare almost blinded her.

Rebecca shut her eyes, but the brightness was still there. And all the time the star continued to grow, until she felt she need only reach out her hand to touch it.

She put out her hand.

There was a whirling curling swirling furling hurling feeling. Rebecca was spinning. The bright white light of the star seemed to dazzle inside her head. There was a high-pitched buzz that made her ears ring.

And then, as suddenly as it had all started, it was over. The brightness inside her head and outside her eyes grew dimmer. The sound faded away.

Rebecca still felt a little dizzy and opened her eyes quickly to stop herself falling over. She looked around. And this was the most curious thing of all.

She was in a place she had never seen before in her life.

It was a room, but unlike any room she had ever seen before.

It was round. Totally round. Round in all directions. In fact it was like being inside a ball. A very big ball. There was no way of telling which was the floor and which were the walls and where the ceiling was.

Rebecca stared. There was a door in what should have been the ceiling and some windows in what could have been the floor, and sitting half-way up what might have been a wall was a man.

All around the man were strange machines and instruments. They had lots of flashing lights and made whirring noises, and looked a bit like the things Rebecca had seen on television science fiction programmes. The man looked extremely angry. He pushed buttons and pulled knobs and turned dials, and the instruments gave off crackling noises and puffs of smoke. Finally, the man pulled one great big switch and all the instruments and lights seemed to die.

The man turned to stare at Rebecca. It was quite obvious that he wasn't pleased with her.

'Wretched child,' he said, in a voice that sounded like chalk scraping on a blackboard. 'Horrid... nasty... wicked... interfering child.'

He got up from his chair and walked down the wall towards her.

'That's clever,' Rebecca thought, 'I wonder how he does that.'

He halted just in front of her and Rebecca was surprised to see that he was much shorter than her. A tiny man and extremely ugly. He had sprouty hair that seemed to grow in several colours, a nose that was a bit like a chicken's beak and a mouth like Poisson, who was Rebecca's goldfish.

He wore a white coat of that kind that men in chemist shops wear, but it was much too long for him and he seemed in danger of tripping over it. He stared at Rebecca through spectacles that looked as if they had been made from the bottom of milk bottles.

'Ooooohhhhh... I hate children,' he said in a spiteful voice. 'Especially those who ruin my experiments and are taller than me.'

'I'm sorry I'm taller than you,' said Rebecca, 'but I can't help it. I'll kneel down if it will make you feel happier.'

So saying, she dropped to her knees and looked him full in the face. She tried to smile. She had often found that a smile was quite helpful when people were cross with her.

'As for ruining your experiment,' she said, 'I don't see how I could have. I've only just arrived... as far as I can tell.'

'Of course you've only just arrived,' the little man snapped. 'You repellent, loathsome horror. You travelled along my transmitter beam and you had no right to! The beam is supposed to *send* people to other planets. Not bring them here.'

He struck his forehead with his clenched fist in a gesture that was supposed to convey extreme frustration. But he did it too hard, and winced with pain.

Rebecca got the feeling that the smile wasn't doing much good, but she kept it on anyway.

'Well I'm sorry,' she said.

'That's all very well,' shrieked the little man, 'but I can't send you back. The beam is all topsy-turvy. It may take me weeks... months... years to get it right. Do you think I'd keep an odious... abominable... impudent child here for a moment longer than I had to?'

The first little chill of fear ran up Rebecca's back like a mouse. 'Do you mean I can't go home?' she asked nervously.

'That's exactly what I mean. You're stuck here!'

Rebecca thought she was going to cry. It's all very well to go somewhere for a visit, but not at all nice when you can't go home. The little man made a strange noise. It was like Cellophane being crumpled up. He was laughing. He was laughing at her.

'Hahahahaha...' went his crinkling laugh. 'You're going to cry. There's nothing I like more than a really unhappy child. The sadder you are the funnier it gets.'

Rebecca tried very hard to stop crying, but two big tears rolled down her cheeks. At the sight of them, the little man clutched his stomach and doubled over with laughter. He fell on the ground and kicked his legs in the air, and laughed and laughed and laughed.

The laughter began to affect her. The little man rolling on the floor, shrieking with mirth, did look very comical. Rebecca started with a little smirk that turned into a smile and then into a chuckle, and a moment later the tears had stopped and she was giggling helplessly.

The man saw she was happy again and stopped laughing. He looked angry.

'Just like a child,' he shouted. 'The moment I start to enjoy myself you go and spoil it by being cheerful. I'm going to work day and night to get my transmitter beam working properly, and the moment it is I'm going to send you back where you came from.'

'That will be fine for me,' Rebecca said, in the same sort of brisk voice that her mother used when she was making a complaint in a shop.

The little man ran back up the wall to his instruments and began to work with a screwdriver. He was still muttering about how he hated children, especially when they were happy, and even more especially when they were both happy *and* taller than him. It was only then Rebecca remembered she was still on her knees.

She stood up. The man gave her a cold stare.

'Well, you can't hang around here,' he said. 'Come back in a week and see how I'm getting on.'

Rebecca glanced up at the door in what should have been the ceiling.

'How do I get out?' she asked. She looked a bit miserable again.

The little man chuckled as he saw her face sadden. 'Walk up to the door, you preposterous, pitiful person,' he yelled delightedly.

'Well,' thought Rebecca, 'here goes.'

She started forward, and to her delight and astonishment found she was able to walk up the side of the room with no trouble at all. She was so pleased by this discovery that she walked straight up on to what should have been the ceiling, right past the door and back down the other side. The odd thing was that even when she was walking across the top of the room, she didn't feel upside down.

'This is a very peculiar world,' she thought to herself, as she started up towards the door again. When she reached it this time, she opened it and stepped outside.

And then very much wished she hadn't.

Terry Nation

Red dragon

A red dragon all alone
lies on top of a wardrobe,
lifeless and unseen,
until a stretching hand touches it awake.

Gently it is guided to the floor
where a quiver of excitement,
an invisible jolt of electricity,
rushes the length of its body.
The red dragon knows it is time
for the weekly 'Sunday spin'.

A short journey to the nearby park
and the dragon is soon
fluttering and stuttering
as it is offered up to the wind.
Then sensing freedom is near,
it puffs out its red chest
and spreads its restless wings
in eager anticipation.

The wind is tempted,
the dragon released,
tossed up towards the sky,
where it gracefully accepts independance
and flies up on to a blue ceiling of sky.
Before long it is
slicing through the clouds,
swooping along the roof-tops
racing over the tree-tops,
rushing across the hills
until finally exhausted
it runs out of breath.

The red dragon now stalls in mid-air
and like some tossed feather in a windless sky,
finds itself slowly spinning, spirally downwards
to topple and tumble across the earth.
There it lies motionless,
sulking with disappointment
at its unexpected and ungainly return.
The only sign of life,
the occasional flick of an angry tail.

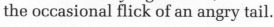

Later that afternoon,
returned to its wardrobe top,
a deflated red dragon lies still and alone.
There it dreams of once again
spreading its paper skin wings
and climbing into a welcoming blue sky
to swank carefree above the earth.
A proud red dragon kite.

Ian Souter

Canal family

On 10 November 1892, Joseph Merchant was almost ten years old, hungry, tired and uncomfortable. He trudged along the muddy tow-path of the Grand Junction Canal. His hob-nailed boots had been handed down and were too big for him. They were rubbing a sore place on his heel.

'Take this rope, our Annie,' he called to his sister. The horse wouldn't pull the narrow boat unless someone walked behind it. Annie gathered up her skirts and jumped from boat to tow-path. Her face was as grimy as Joseph's and her hair hung in lank strands. Keeping clean was difficult. Their mother warmed water on the coal stove and they washed themselves as best they could. They'd never ever had a bath.

The family of six lived in one small cabin where they slept, played, cooked and ate. Most of the boat was for carrying cargo – bricks, cement, stone, to be unloaded at wharves between London and Birmingham.

They were travelling empty on their way to the Coventry Canal to load coal. There were lines of washing strung across the hold. The two younger children chased in and out of the dripping clothes, having somewhere safe to play for once. In bad weather the washing wouldn't dry so the family stayed in dirty clothes for days, sometimes weeks, on end.

The boat passed through Stoke Bruerne locks and headed towards Blisworth Tunnel. Joseph had gone on ahead as always to get the locks ready. The boat mustn't lose any time. He'd be able to open and close lock gates, fill locks, empty locks in his sleep. He worked fast. Time was money and his father had a terrible temper. They got paid by the load for each ton they carried. If they didn't earn, they didn't eat. Often they went hungry, but the horse had to be properly fed to give it energy to pull the heavy boat. Joseph thought the horse had a better life than he did.

You had to be careful when working locks, especially when it was icy or muddy or dark. One of his sisters had slipped and drowned. She was buried in Long Buckby churchyard. His mother took him to see the grave one afternoon while the boat was loading at Buckby Wharf. His fingers traced the letters on her headstone, but he didn't understand what they said. Most canal people couldn't read. His mother couldn't nor his father, nor any of his relations. How could they go to school when they were on the move all the time? It didn't matter, they got by.

The boots were rubbing a blister on Joseph's heel. Not far to walk now. He'd ride the horse over the top while his father and a 'legger' moved the boat through the long tunnel.

There was no tow-path for the horse so the men lay on their backs at the front of the boat on wooden 'wings' and walked the boat through. Joseph's mother steered. The nails in their boots left scratch marks on the walls. It took almost two hours to leg the one and three-quarter miles to the other end of the tunnel.

Joseph's older brothers Isaac and Tom used to do the legging, but they'd left to work a boat of their own. Joseph was going to run away and join them as soon as Annie was big enough to open the locks.

One day he'd buy his own boat and be his own master. He day-dreamed about that boat while he trudged the miles of tow-path. It would be the smartest boat on the cut. The brass rings round the chimney would be polished every day, the paintwork would be kept clean, you'd be able to see every detail on the paintings of roses and castles on the cupboards and water jug. Best of all, on the sides in large lettering would be the owner's name, 'JOSEPH MERCHANT.' But it was just a day-dream.

Life on the canal was easier for Joseph's son, John Merchant. His boat was powered by a diesel engine which towed a butty boat so they could carry twice as much cargo. John and his wife Lily had a cabin in the butty and John's younger brother Ted slept in a small space on the motor boat. In the butty was a cooking range and a pull down table and a bed that folded away into a cupboard. John steered the motor boat and looked after the engine, Lily steered the butty, managing to cook meals at the same time. Ted lockwheeled ahead on his bike to get the locks ready.

The Grand Junction Canal had changed its name to the Grand Union, but there weren't many other changes since John's grandparents' time. The locks were the same, some had been widened to take the motor and the butty side by side, but they worked in the same way. The boats were still brightly decorated with roses and castles, there was the same rush to pick up cargoes and keep moving and still many boat people could not read and write.

John was embarrassed and annoyed having to ask other people to read for him. He made a decision. In 1946 he left the canal and rented a cottage. He

worked at Braunston Dock making rope fenders for the narrow boats. Each day his children went to the village school.

Gradually, year by year, there was less work and fewer boats on the canals. Lorries and trains transported goods to London in a few hours, narrow boats took several days. Weeds started to grow across the waterways, lock gates rotted and tow-paths started to crumble into the water.

John thought the canals were finished. But he was wrong. A new use was found for them.

Jonathan Merchant, aged ten, enjoys his holidays on the Grand Union Canal. The hire boat looks much like the narrow boat his grandparents, John and Lily, used to work except that in the cargo space there is now a bathroom with a shower, two bedrooms, a proper kitchen area and a TV.

They motor through Blisworth Tunnel in just thirty minutes and Jonathan is sure he can pick out the scratch marks made by the leggers' boots. Like his great-grandfather, Joseph, Jonathan Merchant goes on ahead to get the locks ready but he wears a lifejacket and comfortable training shoes.

Joseph Merchant would never have believed that a hundred years on his descendants would pay to go on the canal. He wouldn't have done it without getting paid!

Polly Merchant

The railway children

The very next morning Bobbie began to watch her opportunity to get Peter's engine mended secretly. And the opportunity came the very next afternoon.

Mother went by train to the nearest town to do shopping. When she went there, she always went to the post-office. Perhaps to post her letters to Father, for she never gave them to the children or Mrs Viney to post, and she never went to the village herself. Peter and Phyllis went with her. Bobbie wanted an excuse not to go, but try as she would she couldn't think of a good one. And just when she felt that all was lost, her frock caught on a big nail by the kitchen door and there was a great criss-cross tear all along the front of the skirt. I assure you this was really an accident. So the others pitied her

and went without her, for there was no time for her to change, because they were rather late already and had to hurry to the station to catch the train.

When they had gone, Bobbie put on her everyday frock and went down to the railway. She did not go into the station, but she went along the line to the end of the platform where the engine is when the down train is alongside the platform – the place where there are a water tank and a long limp, leather hose, like an elephant's trunk. She hid behind a bush on the other side of the railway. She had the toy engine done up in brown paper, and she waited patiently with it under her arm.

Then when the next train came in and stopped, Bobbie went across the metals of the up-line and stood beside the engine. She had never been so close to an engine before. It looked much larger and harder than she had expected, and it made her feel very small indeed, and, somehow, very soft – as if she could very, very easily be hurt rather badly.

'I know what silk-worms feel like now,' said Bobbie to herself.

The engine-driver and fireman did not see her. They were leaning out of the other side, telling the porter a tale about a dog and a leg of mutton.

'If you please,' said Roberta – but the engine was blowing off steam and no one heard her.

'If you please, Mr Engineer,' she spoke a little louder, but the engine happened to speak at the same moment, and of course Roberta's soft little voice hadn't a chance.

It seemed to her that the only way would be to climb on to the engine and pull at their coats. The step was high, but she got her knee on it, and clambered into the cab; she stumbled and fell on hands and knees on the base of the great heap of coals that led up to the square opening in the tender. The engine was not above the weaknesses of its fellows; it was making a great deal more noise than there was the slightest need for. And just as Roberta fell on the coals, the engine-driver, who had turned without seeing her, started the engine, and when Bobbie had picked herself up, the train was moving – not fast, but much too fast

for her to get off.

All sorts of dreadful thoughts came to her all together in one horrible flash. There were such things as express trains which went on, she supposed, for hundreds of miles without stopping. Suppose this should be one of them? How would she get home again? She had no money to pay for the return journey.

'And I've no business here. I'm an engine-burglar – that's what I am,' she thought. 'I shouldn't wonder if they could lock me up for this.' And the train was going faster and faster.

There was something in her throat that made it impossible for her to speak. She tried twice. The men had their backs to her. They were doing something to things that looked like taps.

Suddenly she put out her hand and caught hold of the nearest sleeve. The man turned with a start, and he and Roberta stood for a minute looking at each other in silence. Then the silence was broken by them both.

The man said, 'Here's a bloomin' go!' and Roberta burst into tears.

The other man said he was blooming well blest – or something like it – but though naturally surprised they were not exactly unkind.

'You're a naughty little girl, that's what you are,' said the fireman, but the engine-driver said: 'Darling little piece, I call her,' but they made her sit down on an iron seat in the cab and told her to stop crying and tell them what she meant by it.

She did stop, as soon as she could. One thing that helped her was the thought that Peter would give almost his ears to be in her place – on a real engine – really going. The children had often wondered whether any engine-driver could be found noble enough to take them for a ride on an engine – and now here she was. She dried her eyes and sniffed earnestly.

'Now then,' said the fireman, 'out with it. What do you mean by it, eh?'

'Oh, please,' sniffed Bobbie, and stopped.

'Try again,' said the engine-driver, encouragingly.

Bobbie tried again.

'Please, Mr Engineer,' she said, 'I did call out to you from the line, but you didn't hear me – and I just climbed up to touch you on the arm – quite gently I meant to do it – and then I fell into the coals – and I am so sorry if I frightened you. Oh, don't be cross – oh, please don't!' she sniffed again.

'We ain't so much *cross*,' said the fireman, 'as interested like. It ain't every day a little gell tumbles into our coal bunker outer the sky, is it, Bill? What did you *do* it for – eh?'

'That's the point,' agreed the engine-driver; 'what did you do it *for*?'

Bobbie found that she had not quite stopped crying. The engine-driver patted her on the back and said: 'Here, cheer up, Mate. It ain't so bad as all that 'ere, I'll be bound.'

'I wanted,' said Bobbie, much cheered to find herself addressed as 'Mate' – 'I only wanted to ask you if you'd be so kind as to mend this.' She picked up the brown-paper parcel from among the coals and undid the string with hot, red fingers that trembled.

Her feet and legs felt the scorch of the engine fire, but her shoulders felt the wild chill rush of the air. The engine lurched and shook and rattled, and as they shot under a bridge the engine seemed to shout in her ears.

The fireman shovelled on coals.

Bobbie unrolled the brown paper and disclosed the toy engine.

'I thought,' she said wistfully, 'that perhaps you'd mend this for me – because you're an engineer, you know.'

The engine-driver said he was blowed if he wasn't blest.

'I'm blest if I ain't blowed,' remarked the fireman.

But the engine-driver took the little engine and looked at it – and the fireman ceased for an instant to shovel coal, and looked, too.

'It's like your precious cheek,' said the engine-driver – 'whatever made you think we'd be bothered tinkering penny toys?'

'I didn't mean it for precious cheek,' said Bobbie, 'only everybody that has anything to do with railways is so kind and good. I didn't think you'd mind. You don't really – do you?' she added, for she had seen a not unkindly wink pass between the two.

'My trade's driving of a engine, not mending her – especially such a hout-size as this 'ere,' said Bill.

'An' 'ow are we a-goin' to get you back to your sorrowing friends and relations, and all be forgiven and forgotten?'

'If you'll put me down next time you stop,' said Bobbie, firmly, though her heart beat fiercely against her arm as she clasped her hands, 'and lend me the money for a third-class ticket, I'll pay you back – honour bright. I'm not a confidence trick like in the newspapers – really, I'm not.'

'You're a little lady, every inch,' said Bill, relenting suddenly and completely. 'We'll see you get home safe. An' about this engine – Jim – ain't you got ne'er a pal as can use a soldering iron? Seems to me that's about all the little bounder wants doing to it.'

'That's what Father said,' Bobbie explained eagerly. 'What's that for?'

She pointed to a little brass wheel that he had turned as he spoke.

'That's the injector.'

'In – what?'

'Injector to fill up the boiler.'

'Oh,' said Bobbie, mentally registering the fact to tell the others; 'that is interesting.'

'This 'ere's the automatic brake,' Bill went on, flattered by her enthusiasm. 'You just move this 'ere little handle – do it with one finger, you can – and the train jolly soon stops. That's what they call the Power of Science in the newspapers.'

He showed her two little dials, like clock faces, and told her how one showed how much steam was going, and the other showed if the brake was working properly.

By the time she had seen him shut off steam with a big shining steel handle, Bobbie knew more about the inside working of an engine than she had ever thought there was to know, and Jim had promised that his second cousin's wife's brother should solder the toy engine, or Jim would know the reason why. Besides all the knowledge she had gained Bobbie felt that she and Bill and Jim were now friends for life, and that they had wholly and forever forgiven her for stumbling uninvited among the sacred coals of their tender.

At Stacklepoole Junction she parted from them with warm expressions of mutual regard. They handed her over to the guard of a returning train – a friend of theirs – and she had the joy of knowing what guards do in their secret fastnesses, and understood how when you pull the communication cord in railway carriages, a wheel goes round under the guard's nose and a loud bell rings in his ears. She asked the guard why his van smelt so fishy, and learned that he had to carry a lot of fish every day, and that the wetness in the hollows of the corrugated floor had all drained out of boxes full of plaice and cod and mackerel and soles and smelts.

Bobbie got home in time for tea, and she felt as though her mind would burst with all that had been put into it since she parted from the others. How she blessed the nail that had torn her frock!

'Where have you been?' asked the others.

'To the station, of course,' said Roberta.

E. Nesbit

Flying to India

And so we climbed inside the plane,
Sam, Alice and I,
to sit in the sky – to fly
all the way over the side of the world
to India
was our adventure.

FASTEN YOUR SEAT-BELTS!
They fastened the door,
the engines behind us,
the runways before,
and, lurching gently,
we started to creep
as low as a moth
on the kitchen floor –
to wait our turn
where, large and small,
as if it was apparatus-day
in a giant machines' school hall,
the aeroplanes queue
for the take-off run,
one by one.

The Jumbo's gone –
and now it's us!
Like a boiling kettle
at the whistle
the engines screaming,
we're off! We're running
the wide white road
like a galloping horse
the last fence ahead,
faster and faster,
so heavy inside
you could feel her gather up
all of her power
to hurl her metal
and all her load,
clumsy and loud,
at the thin light air –
nothing can stop us!
Up goes the nose,
and the people in front of us

tilting backwards
nearly on top of us,
things bump and jolt,
and through the window –
look, there's a roof,
and Windsor Castle!
Magical racehorse, horse of metal,
far did your proud jump go!

They brought us strange food,
black-haired ladies
in blood-red blouses
with smiling faces,
and tiny paper packets of pepper,
salt, milk powder, toothpicks and sugar –
we picked and poked, we sprinkled and stirred,
and ate,
and drank:
enchanted food
it might have been,
for we saw what we had never seen.

For when I looked out,
I saw the sea
Stretch like a fan,
edging the land
far, far below, and nothing between –
I saw England's roots, pale roots of sand
going down deep through the rich blue water,
and all the waves between England and France
so long and still,
you could count them all.

Suddenly we bucked and stumbled,
I was afraid, I thought aeroplanes never trembled
What's happened?
A wisp like a ghost brushed by –
it was just a bump in the road of the sky!
Thick air and thin, air rising and falling:
strange road,
made of so much nothing!
Overhead
it was brilliant blue –
but under us now
there began to gather
a fat froth, milky and thick, until

on an endless carpet of cotton-wool,
we were alone, so small,
Like a lonely fly, upstairs in an empty room –
then we dipped through.

Down the ceiling we came, to a land
where tiny square houses stood neat in a row,
no bigger than dolls' houses for dolls,
by a road like a ruler,
and coming and going,
matchbox lorries, pin-men's cars,
none of them knowing
that we could see!
We stopped for breath, it was Germany.

Night poured round us
and on we went,
in black, to Rome,
where the floor was swept.
The engines hurt, they roared at our ears so loud –
and at last we slept.

Somewhere behind us, far away,
our street lay
tucked in that shadow-bed
of night –
but though the dark held on to our tail,
we ran ahead,
ran, till we overtook time, meeting the next day
half-way, straight for the sun's big apricot,
and first for us the golden light,
showing the way!

O we were flying above a brown country:
brown rocks, brown sand, and not a tree
or field or town that we could see,
but a thin road, going on and on
through the dreary deserts of Iran.
We grew weary, bored, tired,
sitting so long
stuck in the air –
How much longer till we get there?

Deserts and mountains passed,
and then, at last,
the world spread open a vast

yellowy greeny blue check table-cloth,
bunches of villages set among the squares,
and the pilot, his voice all fuzzy,
announced where we were –
it was India!

Lovely were the clouds
the day put up to greet us,
white twists of barley-sugar,
curly locks of hair –
it was dinner-time when we landed there.
Now over fields with wavy edges
and felt-open hills with furry faces
under a cloud like a scarf we flew –
it was brown beneath white beneath blue –
when suddenly, higher than us, one after
another, above the cloud, we saw,
like planets unknown to the world below,
dazzling black rocks and bright snow –
peaks of the giant Himalayas,
shining, as if they'd come out to see us!

This was the country our ticket promised,
and as we came in to land –
we could see our friends there to meet us –
Look! There's Chris and Moraig and Hamish!
We touched the ground,
we laughed and shouted and ran
in the fresh wind and the warm sun!

Empty, forgotten,
the magical horse lay dumb.

Libby Houston

One long step

It was one of those nights,
lights showed in every window.
History was in the making
and nobody wanted to miss it,
except Mother, that is. By
one o'clock in the morning

she'd had enough. She left
the three of us to keep vigil
by the television set. We
made coffee, more coffee, ate
toasted cheese, replenished
the fire. Dad sucked on
an empty pipe. I dozed
on and off and my daughter
caught up with her homework.

The NASA control room became
our own. We haunted the bank
of flickering screens, grew
familiar with each scientist,
posture, profile, laconic voice.
Time ticked away. Tension
leaked out. When we had all
but given up, it happened.
Apollo appeared, floated down,
settled on the moon like a hen
on her nest, in a flurry of dust.
NASA erupted into a blitz of
cheering. And yet, calm voices
still talked on, encouraging,
advising. Another long wait.

The door opened. Neil Armstrong
made his well-rehearsed speech.
We watched the two figures, like
ghostly Michelin men, bounce and
dance across the grey surface
of the moon. We yawned, stretched,
gathered up used mugs, switched
off the television set. Dad
and I, wide awake, walked
to the front gate. Stars paled
to daisy petals in the early
morning sky and the moon hung
on its usual hook. But for us
it was no longer an old man's face
smiling down on a sleeping world.

Moira Andrew

BACK IN TIME

Charlotte's first hay-ride

Charlotte watched as the moon flicked fingers of light through the tiny window, and on to the dress.

Gran had hummed happily as she'd hung it on the wardrobe door.

'Tomorrow, Charlotte, tomorrow you'll be a proper little lady in this,' she'd smiled, before tucking her in and switching off the light.

Charlotte was anything but happy as she stared into the darkness from the hollow of the marshmallow mattress. At very nearly seven years old dressing up was not her idea of fun — especially dressing up in dresses! Wellies and jeans, and mud, was what Charlotte Orchard liked — and weekend visits to her grandparents' farm usually meant plenty of that.

But this time it was going to be different.

A hay-ride, Grandpa had said. A hay-ride, on Sunday. And Charlotte had pictured all the bales in the yard chugging off down the lane, like a train.

But no. It would be a grand parade, he'd told her. A parade of horses and wagons, and people dressed in old-fashioned clothes.

'A hundred years ago,' Grandpa had said, 'after hay-making, the farmers would paint their wagons in yellows and reds, as though to say "thank you" to the sun, then they'd tie ribbons and flowers and bells to the horses, and polish up their harness brasses until the sun bounced off like golden arrows heading for heaven.'

'Are we going to do that?' Charlotte had asked, pulling a puzzled face.

'You bet, Charlie, you bet. Then we'll dress up like they did. I'll wear a top hat, and a coat with two tails....'

'Can I wear a top hat?'

'Ladies,' Grandpa had pretended

to be stern, 'ladies wear bonnets, and pretty frocks right down to their ankles, and they carry parasols!' But his eyes had twinkled as he'd gone on to tell how they would ride in a long, long line of wagons – all colour and clatter and chatter.

And then he seemed to drift off into a dream. But Charlotte wasn't dreaming. She was still wide awake in the big bed where Gran had tucked her in before switching off the light. And she watched as the moon flicked fingers of light through the tiny window, and on to the dress – and the shadows filled out the folds and flounces of that Sunday-best dress that belonged to somebody else – to somebody from long, long ago. And Charlotte knew she wasn't dreaming.

Next morning, Sunday, she woke long before the church bells. They were still sound asleep when she pulled on jeans and wellies and went to find Grandpa in the stables.

The smell of horses and hay tickled her nostrils. At first, in the dim light, all Charlotte could see were four pairs of long, white feathery socks, until slowly, the legs they belonged to took shape, and so did four huge, round, brown bottoms. There were shuffles and swishes, and feet the size of dinner plates were stamped, as Agnes and Bruno, Bonny and Dan snuffled velvet muzzles into their breakfast bran.

'You going to help me, Charlie?' Grandpa asked, coming in with a box full of brushes and combs and sponges, and a bucket bubbling over with soapy water.

'Let's have you up here,' and with that he swung Charlotte astride Bonny's broad back, handed up a silvery comb and taught her to tease the tangles from the mare's mane.

They groomed and plaited, and

he reached up to wash four kind, white faces, and every time a horse snorted or shifted, Charlotte felt she would slip and slither right down their shiny sides.

But this was fun! Getting the horses ready to pull the bright wagon on its steel-rimmed wheels – getting greasy and hairy, hot and smelly and dusty – was great fun!

Charlotte sulked when it was *her* turn to get ready. She was not going to be washed and groomed and plaited and dressed in pink frills and petticoats – not when she was very, very nearly seven years old. And sulks turned into tantrums and Gran huffed and puffed and cried, 'You look like you live up a chimney, Charlotte Orchard! What are we going to do with you?' This seemed to give Grandpa an idea. He stopped trying to tie his tie and rushed out to the barn – with the black-streaked, tear-stained, barefoot Charlotte in tow.

Under a heap of sacks he found a chimney sweep's brush, half bald but bristling with cobwebs, and flicking a flat cap from a nail in the wall, he plonked it on Charlotte's head.

'Now come with me, young madam,' and grabbing a halter they hurried round to the paddock. Here was the muddiest, scruffiest, cheekiest pony Charlotte had ever seen.

'Charlie one, meet Charlie two.' Grandpa made them rub noses.

So Charlie one, dressed as a Victorian chimney boy, and Charlie two, dressed as a very dirty seventh birthday present, happily joined in the parade, and that day they were decorated with a red rosette – for having the very best costume in the hay-ride.

Gina Douthwaite

The last one off the Ark

Now I'll bet you know the story of Noah, and how he built an Ark to save his family and all the animals in the world from The Great Flood.

But what you don't know is that life on board the Ark was actually... *terrible*. It was smelly, and cold, and the sea was always stormy, which meant that everyone felt seasick.

The Ark was also crowded, and there were many arguments. The Noah family spent most of their time separating angry animals. And when they weren't doing that, they argued with each other.

So they were *very* pleased when the waters went down, and the Ark settled on dry land once more.

'Thank goodness that's over!' said Noah. 'Now hurry up and open those doors, will you?'

There was a massive stampede for the exit, and after a lot of pushing and shoving, the Ark was empty. Well... almost.

Noah and Mrs Noah were just getting ready to disembark when Ham, their oldest son, came running into the cabin.

'Mum and Dad,' he said, 'you'd better come quickly. One of the animals doesn't want to leave.'

'Oh, doesn't he?' said Noah, crossly, and stomped off. 'I'll soon see about that.'

Noah's other two sons, Shem and Japheth, were waiting in the hold with their wives. Ham's wife was there too, sitting on a pile of straw with a small, golden, furry creature in her lap.

'What's going on down here?' boomed Noah.

'Ssh!' said Ham's wife. 'Can't you see he's frightened?'

'Frightened?' said Noah. 'What's he got to be scared of?'

'You, for a start!' said Mrs Noah. She was right. The small creature was looking at Noah with eyes as wide as saucers.

'Poor little thing,' said Ham's wife. 'He's only a baby. I'll bet he got left behind in the rush. What sort of animal *is* he?'

'How should I know?' said Noah, peering at the creature. 'Anyway, that's not important. You do realise *we* can't get off until *he* does, don't you?'

The others hadn't thought about that. But now they saw it was a real problem. So the Noah family followed their usual plan for deciding something important.

They argued at great length in very loud voices.

'Hold on a minute,' said Mrs Noah at last. 'This is only making things worse. Why don't we just leave him alone for a while and see what happens?'

And that's exactly what they did.

Noah, Mrs Noah, their three sons, and their three wives all crept off and hid.

They waited... and they waited... and they waited....

And nothing happened.

The little creature stayed exactly where he was. He just seemed puzzled.

'This isn't working,' said Noah impatiently to Mrs Noah. 'Got any more bright ideas?'

'I have, as a matter of fact,' said Mrs Noah with a sniff.

She laid a trail of tasty titbits from the pile of straw to the doors. Everyone watched as the small creature's nose started to twitch.

They held their breath as the baby animal ate the first titbit, then the second, the third, the fourth, the fifth....

Within a few minutes he had reached the last one. He put a paw on the gangplank leading down to the ground. Before him lay a damp, cold, windy world full of mud and puddles.

He took one look, then turned and scampered back to his warm straw.

After that they tried walking off the Ark one at a time, then all together, to show the little creature what to do. They tried talking to him. They tried drawing him a map. They tried begging and pleading. Noah even tried crying.

But nothing worked.

By now Noah was in despair.

'That animal is *never* going to leave,' he muttered. 'There's a great big world waiting for us out there, but we'll be stuck on this horrible boat forever... and will you *please* stop tugging at my sleeve like that, Ham!'

'But look, Dad!' said Ham. 'I think our problem's solved!'

While Noah had been talking, a large animal had returned to the Ark. She walked over to the small creature, gently picked him up in her jaws – and simply carried him out.

'I do hope he'll be all right,' said Ham's wife.

'He'll be fine!' boomed Noah. 'And now, as the last one's off the Ark, can we get going ourselves? We've plenty to do!'

The little creature *was* fine. Oh yes, and if you're still wondering, he was... a lion cub. He grew up to be King of the Beasts, and was frightened of nothing. Especially grumpy old men with big beards and loud voices!

Tony Bradman

Powder-monkey

You don't see a ghost every day of the week, not a real live – I mean dead – ghost. Nor a powder-monkey. James and Catherine didn't know what a powder-monkey was, but they knew a ghost when they saw one.

It happened in Portsmouth.

'Pompey, that's our name for Portsmouth,' Dad said, as they drove down the last long hill into that sprawling town by the sea. 'My family's been here for generations, in the dockyards and in the navy. Pompey's a naval town – Royal Navy.'

'Can we see the *Victory*, Dad, can we?' squealed Catherine, twisting this way and that in her seat, hoping to spy the tall masts of a sailing ship in the forest of cranes and gantries of the harbour.

'You promised,' said James, munching a bag of chicken-flavoured crisps. 'You have to keep your promises.'

Dad sighed. 'Yes, James, I don't need you to tell me that. Anyway, I want to see *Victory* again myself.'

'It was Nelson's flagship,' said James.

'Yes, James,' said Dad.

'At Trafalgar,' said James.

'It's ever so big!' Catherine bent her neck backwards looking up from the quayside to the stateroom windows of the *Victory*. 'It's like a church at the back, all windows.'

Dad laughed. 'Sixty-nine metres long – that's tiny compared to a modern battleship made of steel and iron. *Victory* is nearly all wood. It hasn't got an engine, just those three masts for the sails. And the back of a ship is called the stern.'

'The front is called the prow,' said James, his mouth full of ice-cream cornet.

'Quite right. And the shield on the prow with the Royal Coat of Arms....'

'Is the figurehead.' Ice-cream gone.

'Yes, James.'

The outside of *Victory* was striped in orange and black. The orange stripes were the gun decks, three floors inside the ship like layers of a cake, each with a row of square holes, each hole a gun port with a black cannon barrel poking out.

'*Victory* has 104 guns,' their guide told them. 'They were not very powerful and when the ship was rolling they were hard to aim. To make a hole in the side of an enemy ship, *Victory* had to sail as close as she could – side by side was best.'

Inside the gun decks it was dark and dusty. Dad banged his head on one of the wooden beams that ran across the ceiling. When the guide said that there were 850 sailors aboard at the battle of Trafalgar, Catherine and James began to realise how small and crowded *Victory* really would have been.

'The sailors slept between the cannons,' the guide told them. 'Each had less than a metre of shoulder space. They didn't have beds like us – that would have taken up far too much room. They slept in hammocks – canvas sheets held up by ropes stretched from one wooden beam to another.'

'I can't imagine either of you two in one of those!' laughed Dad, and he hurried after the guide.

'Come on,' Catherine said to her brother. 'We're getting left behind.'

'I want to have a closer look at the guns.'

That was when they saw the ghost.

'It's a boy, a little boy...' Catherine said.

'And you can see right through him!' said James.

'I'm not a little boy. I'm twelve years old and my name's Harry. I haven't seen you before.' The boy looked at Catherine. 'Are you a powder-monkey?'

'What's that?' she asked.

'Powder-monkeys fetch the gunpowder for the gunners. Boys like me are powder-monkeys, sometimes girls, women really. You have to be little and quick or you get blown to bits.' He pointed at James. 'He'd get blown to bits.'

'Well, you can talk....'

'Don't mind him, he's only my brother James. I'm Catherine. We're visitors.'

Harry cocked his head and sniffed the air. 'It's gone quiet. The battle must be over.'

'What battle?' James was interested in battles.

'Against the Spanish and French, of course, off the coast of Spain at Cape Trafalgar.'

'Trafalgar,' breathed Catherine 'Lord Nelson was killed at the battle of Trafalgar.'

'Aye, more's the pity. It's a sad day for the British fleet, for all that we won a glorious victory.'

Catherine asked thoughtfully. 'What date is it? What year?'

'Why 21 October 1805, of course. You are a ninny.'

'It's just history to us.'

Harry shook his head sadly. 'It'll go down in history, that's for sure, but I'll not forget the heat and the smoke and the noise, cannon firing, wood splintering, my friends hurt and crying out for help. Lord Nelson in his fine uniform, shot by a marksman from high in the rigging of a French ship.'

'We're sorry you're so unhappy,' said Catherine.

'Part of me is unhappy,' said Harry, 'but part of me is proud. All our sailors were very brave. Especially the Admiral. We all loved Lord Nelson. He was a good commander. He hardly ever flogged anybody.'

Harry walked towards James and Catherine. Through his thin body they could see the mighty black cannon, the piles of shot, the ramrods and the wooden buckets in which they were cooled. They weren't afraid of Harry, not now they'd spoken to him.

'Let me show you my ship,' he said, and glided down the gangway, making no sound on the creaky timber floor. James and Catherine looked at each other and followed.

'You've seen where we slept – well, this is the Admiral's room.' Harry showed them into a large room at the stern of the ship. '*Victory* was Lord Nelson's flagship. From here he commanded the captains of the fleet. *Victory* had its own captain, Captain Hardy.'

'I've heard of him!' Catherine exclaimed. 'Nelson said, "Kiss me, Hardy," to him before he died.'

'Everybody knows that!' said James.

Catherine walked across the stateroom. 'Look, we're on the other side of those windows, the ones like a church.'

James was in a side room looking at a bed with drapes like a large cot. 'Is this Lord Nelson's? It's not very big.'

'He was small,' said Harry, 'and not always well. He lost his right arm when he was wounded many years ago, and he was always sea-sick.'

'Just like Dad,' giggled Catherine. 'He gets sick on a boating lake.'

'I'm sure I read somewhere that Nelson was blind in one eye,' said James, 'and he put his telescope to his blind eye and said "I do not see the signal".'

Harry laughed. 'Aye,' he said, 'that's true enough. He did it at the battle of Copenhagen when he was being told to stop the fight. The Admiral always wanted his own way. He sent a message of his own at Trafalgar.'

'We know it!' Catherine and James both wanted to be the one to say Nelson's words.

'Aye,' interrupted Harry, 'but do you know that the signalman helped Lord Nelson make up the message? Some words take more flags than others.'

'Like a code,' said Catherine.

'That's right. The Admiral wanted it done quickly so the message was...' and they all sang out, '"England expects that every man will do his duty",' and they laughed with pleasure.

They pressed on along gangways and up and down ladders between

Victory's decks, and arrived at the magazines.

'This is where we collect the gunpowder cartridges.' The room was feebly lit by candle-light coming through a glass window from another room. 'So we won't be blown to bits,' laughed Harry.

They went on to a small room that had tall wooden cabinets and racks with blunt and rusty looking tools.

'This is the safest part of the ship in a battle,' said Harry, 'right in the middle where no shot would reach. That's why the doctor's surgery is here.'

'It's painted red,' Catherine whispered.

'To hide the blood,' said James in a hollow voice.

Harry sighed. 'D'you see that big cask? Lord Nelson was brought back to England in that cask, filled with brandy to preserve his body. Then he was given a great funeral and buried at St Paul's Cathedral in London.'

James and Catherine ran their hands over the rough wood of the cask, imagining the dead man inside, floating pale and fish-like, his mouth open in the liquid. They shivered.

'There's a story,' James whispered to Catherine, 'that after they took the body out, the sailors drank the brandy.'

'I don't believe it,' Catherine replied with a snort.

'Admiral Nelson was twelve, just like me, when he first went to sea. He was forty-seven when he died.

Come on and I'll show you where he was standing when he was shot,' said Harry.

He led them up a ladder to the quarterdeck at the stern of the ship. As they approached the daylight, Harry hesitated, growing faint in the brightness. 'You go ahead,' he said to Catherine and James.

They saw a small brass plaque set in the wooden deck. Getting close they read the message. It said, 'Here Nelson fell, 21 October, 1805.'

So you've caught up with us at last.' Dad came up to them, speaking crossly. 'A fine pair you are, worrying me to see *Victory* and then missing everything.'

'We saw it all,' said James.

'And we had our own guide,' said Catherine. 'Harry showed us round.'

She turned to introduce Dad to the powder-monkey.

But Harry was gone.

Alan Brown

A candle in the dark

Charlie Padgett ducked into the tunnel and gave his new apprentice a heavy shove. 'Get a move on, will ye? We're late at the face as it is!' Jimmy stumbled forward into the dark, stubbing his toes on the metal rail which ran along the muddy floor. He recovered himself and went slowly forward, his hands out in front of him. The light from Padgett's lamp barely penetrated the darkness: a darkness so palpable that it felt like solid matter. The boy cried out as his head struck something in the roof, and he staggered, clutching at the rough wall for support. Padgett, coming up behind, spat a curse and aimed a kick at Jimmy's shin, so that he cried out again. 'Keep yer feet, yer clumsy brat!' he growled. 'And ger a move on!'

Jimmy put up a blackened hand to rub the sore place on his head. 'It's very low,' he said. 'And narrow.'

Padgett grunted. 'This is the main road. Wait till ye ger in the workings!'

The floor had a slight upward slope, and as they walked, the mud gave way to a dry rubble and dust. Jimmy winced as his naked foot came down on to something sharp. The balls of his feet felt raw. 'Don't kick rubble over the rails,' said Padgett. 'Derail a corve and I'll bray ye all round the pit!' Jimmy made no reply, but plunged on. It was becoming hot. He could hear voices, somewhere up ahead. His master's hand gripped his shoulder, halting him. 'We turn here,' he grunted. 'Up the side-gate and through to the other main road. Remember this, for ye'll be hurryin' this way soon.'

A narrower tunnel led off to their left, and they entered it. This time Padgett went first. There was no slope here, and no rails. They went a few paces, then Padgett stopped, holding up his lamp. The light revealed a solid wooden gate, blocking the tunnel. 'Open up, Joe, ye idle whelp!' he cried savagely. 'Every time I come up this gate I catch ye sleeping.'

Jimmy screwed his eyes into the dark. He could see nobody at first, but Padgett swung his lamp and the light spilled into an opening, a hole in the wall. At the back of this hole squatted Trapper Joe. His hole was not high enough for him to sit up straight and he squatted with his back hunched and his head forward.

'Was not sleepin', Mr Padgett,' he said in a frightened voice. 'Was lookin' t'other way.'

'One day ye'll be lookin' t'other way when something hits ye!' growled Padgett. 'Come on – get this thing out of my way!' Joe hauled on the gate, which slid heavily into the hole until its end pinned him to the back wall, and the way was clear. Padgett went through with the lamp and the hole was plunged into utter darkness. As Jimmy made to follow his master, Joe's voice came out of the gloom.

'This is trappin', master Jimmy. How d'ye like it?'

'It... it's very dark,' said Jimmy, 'and you must be lonely here by yourself. Don't they let you have a candle?'

A chuckle, eerily disembodied. 'No candle: candles cost money.' Jimmy stumbled, following the lamp.

They came out into the other main road. There were rails again. As they came out of the side-gate a tram was coming along the rails. It was piled high with coal and there was a candle stuck on the front of it with a lump of mud. When it reached the side-gate, the boy who was pushing it came round to the front and eased it off the rails; first the front wheels, then the back. He was panting, and his near-naked body glistened with black sweat. He paid no attention to the watchers, but got behind his corve again and, pushing with hands and head, disappeared into the side-gate. 'Don't stand there gawping!' shouted Padgett. 'That's one corve off already, and we haven't started yet!' They went on. Jimmy's back hurt from stooping, and his feet were cut and sore. He felt as though he had been in the pit for hours, though he knew it could have only been minutes. He kept seeing in his head a picture of little Joe, alone in that black hole. He shuddered.

As they went slowly onward, Jimmy saw a number of very low, narrow tunnels leading off into the black wall on his left. He could hear voices, and when he crouched to look into one of the tunnels he saw light gleaming, dully, deep inside. Padgett glanced back and saw the boy's wondering expression.

'Workings,' he grunted. 'Ours is just up ahead.'

After a few more yards Padgett stopped, and Jimmy thought that they

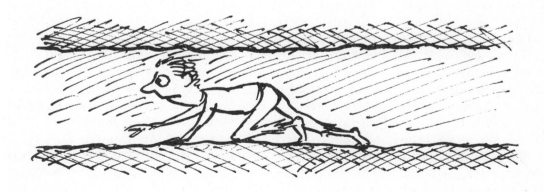

must have reached their destination. Padgett beckoned him forward and pointed to a hole in the glistening black wall. 'This is an abandoned working,' he said. There was menace in his voice. 'Dangerous. The roof-props are cracking and the roof could cave in at any time. Whatever happens, yer never to go into that working. Do ye understand?' His fingers dug into the boy's shoulder, like last night outside the tavern. Jimmy gritted his teeth.

'Yes sir,' he gasped. 'Trapper Joe told me.'

Padgett glanced at him sharply. 'Told ye? Told ye what?' The grip tightened.

'Not to go in. He said other boys might dare me,' said Jimmy squirming under the iron fingers.

'Trapper Joe has too much trap!' snarled Padgett. 'I'll not have ye talking to him. And think on: keep out of closed road.'

Presently, they came to Padgett's working. The big man dropped on all-fours and crawled in. Jimmy followed. It was so narrow in the working that Padgett's shoulders scraped the walls as he moved forward, and his cap rasped along the jagged roof.

As he crawled, Jimmy felt a sensation through his whole body as though insupportable weight was bearing him down on him from above, and inward on all sides. He wanted desperately to stand up: to throw out his arms and feel no walls. To toss back his head and see the sky. He wanted to run with the wind in his face. He felt that if he did not get out he would die. And he knew that he could never get out.

Robert Swindells

Thorkell Fairhair

The fjord was full of the noise of busy men. The very air seemed to vibrate as in a great open-air smithy. The clanging of anvil-blows, the hammering of planks, the buzzing of long two-handed saws echoed and re-echoed across the enclosed blue water. And all these sounds seemed to glance like flat stones over the surface of the sea-valley, to lose themselves up the farther rocky slopes and then in the great dim forests that crowned the rim of the inlet and stretched far away into the mountains, into the unknown frightening spaces of trolls and witches.

The little thatch and wooden settlement that straggled along the shore of the fjord throbbed with activity. Black-faced men in leather aprons worked the great ox-skin bellows to fan the flames of many outdoor furnaces; others beat out long iron nails on anvils that were gripped between their padded knees; yet others walked backwards down long rope-walks, twisting the harsh fibres in their raw hands. The women worked busily stitching, with thick waxed thread, or at the shuttles of their looms, which were set up outside the hovel doors so as to make the most of the new and welcome spring light. Children scurried back and forth, fetching and carrying for

their sweating elders, sometimes a hammer, or a pail of ice-cold water to temper the iron, sometimes a roughly-cut hunk of barley bread or a pannikin of corn-wine.

All worked in that place, even the very old and the crippled. The ship they were building was not the toy of one man; it was the property of them all. And it was almost finished. Another day at the most would see it ready for the painters. Even the oldest ones, plaiting thongs, horny-handed in the shadow, saw new dreams of gold taking shape before their dim eyes. 'Share and share alike,' thought they. 'To each his portion, and may she speed well and return laden before I make my greetings to Odin.' This longship had been built by the whole village. Those who were skilled in shipbuilding had worked day by day, with an adze on the planks or walking backwards along the rope-walks. Those who had no such skill, or were too old to wield an axe or to ply a needle, had contributed in other ways, either by supplying food and drink to their more active neighbours, or by paying good money to shipwrights to come from afar.... And all this, so that the ship should bring back profit to the village. These men did not think of glory, or even of adventure. They were practical men – as most northerners are – who wanted a good return for their labour or money. And the ship which they were creating would bring back those good returns, they hoped. This village had heard of the rich court of the Franks. They had seen the fine silks and the painted pictures that had come from Byzantium. And such English noblemen as had crossed the northern seas to them had worn gold about their necks and arms.... The rest of the world must be very rich, they thought.

And so they built this longship, to relieve the rest of the world of some of its surplus riches. The village on the fjord could do with a little gold, and some silks. It would not even object to a few pictures – provided, of course, that the artist had used real gold leaf in painting them!

Among all these fjord-folk, the longship lay on her runway like a royal thing, a proud princess whose slaves attended to her every want. A longship that would brave the harsh buffeting of the open seas, or out-trick the subtlest of rivers. A handsome shell in which a warrior king would feel proud to drift out on an ebb tide, the death-flames licking round him as he lay among his furs and his weapons and his hounds, on that last long journey to Odin's feast-hall.

Of clean and fresh-smelling oak, the longship was almost eighty feet long, from stem to stern, and sixteen feet broad at her middle. Standing over seven feet high from keel-bottom to gunwales, she dwarfed the many busy men who toiled about her on the stocks, even though as yet her forty-foot mast had not been stepped into its socket in the keel. They smiled at each other, satisfied with their work. If the good weather held, they would step the mast tomorrow, so that it would fall backwards quickly and easily when the forestay was eased off. And tomorrow, by the help of all the gods in the groves, they would fit the other ropes, the stays to prow and stern, those that braced the long yard-arm, those that ran on pulleys to raise and lower the sail....

The foreman of the shipwrights wiped a rough and work-soiled hand over his red face. He turned to the apprentice lad who caulked the smart clinker-built planking of the sides.

'Never was a maiden more comely,' he said.

The boy grinned back at him. 'Maybe you are right, Master Björn,' he said. 'My aunt and my sisters have woven the sail for her, and a fine thing it is – all red and blue and green, in great stripes the thickness of a pine-trunk.'

'Ay, and your mother has embroidered the pennant, hasn't she lad?' said Björn, smiling.

The boy looked down, as though he knew not what to say. 'Well master,' he ventured at last, 'she has edged it and put on its long golden fringe, but no one has told her what emblem to work on the white silk. It rests as unmarked as the snow on the Bear Mountain. We know not what name she shall carry.'

He glanced at Björn craftily, as though expecting his master to give him the answer. But Björn only whistled and bent to examine a row of rivets and their great square washers that held the long oak planks fast together.

'Ay, ay,' he said, in a whisper, 'who knows what she will be named!'

The boy was suddenly conscious of a hush about him. He stopped working and bent towards Björn. 'Here is the one, master, who will know, if anyone does.'

Björn turned and then pulled his forelock, and, like all the other workmen, stood silent and waiting. And among the huts by the blue water a name was whispered that fetched the young maids to the doorways, and put a smile on the faces of the older women.

'Thorkell Fairhair! Thorkell Fairhair!'

In the shadow of one hut an old man sat, patiently mending a fish-net. His hands were gnarled and twisted with rheumatism, but he forced them on and on, to tie the knots in the tarry twine. A long sword-cut had once ploughed the length of his cheek and had taken away the teeth on one side of his jaw. He heard the name, this old warrior, and a shiver seemed to pass over his face like a little cloud before the sun. His battle-scarred face wrinkled along its war-cuts in a strange, ironic smile.

Henry Treece

Remembrance of things past

During a recent visit to the Lancashire town where I was born, I set off, armed with a tape-recorder, to the homes of two of my elderly relatives. I wanted to ask them some questions about life in the Victorian and Edwardian schools of Wigan.

Gran, Elsie Yates Austin, was born in 1901 and left school in 1914 when she was thirteen. Attending school only until the age of thirteen was the norm in those days. Very few were privileged to attend any form of secondary school.

Aunt May is well into her nineties and was born in 1895. She also left school at thirteen, but in contrast to my Gran, Aunt May liked school. Gran says that she herself was not a success but that Aunt May was.

Both women seemed very much aware that at that time they were treated as if they were the property of their fathers, who had the right to decide when they left school and when they went to work.

Gran told me, 'When I left school at thirteen my dad said I hadn't to go out to work for another twelve months. So I used to do my mum's sewing for her and baby-sit. At night I'd bath the baby and put it to bed. One day, the mill owner's wife came to my mother and she said, "There's an opening for a cutting job at the mill, cutting out baby clothes. We were wondering whether Elsie would like it."

'My mum replied, that I'd have to have my dad's consent. He agreed and that was how I got a job. I worked until I was expecting your dad.'

For women at this time, marriage was the end of their career and education.

'You didn't think beyond that,' was my Gran's comment.

Gran seems perfectly happy with this state of affairs and seems to have had a good relationship with her dad. In contrast, Aunt May is still very bitter about the circumstances which led to her leaving school and what her dad decided. She told me: 'I remember when I was twelve years old my dad wanted me to go half-time. You could do that in those days if you'd so many marks. Well, the headmaster sent for him to go up to the school and he said to my father: "Do you know Mr Austin, you are spoiling your daughter's education. She's one of my brightest pupils, and I have great hopes for her." That sticks in my mind. I think if that was happening now I'd have gone to college. I was clever. My dad wanted me to leave school. Imagine how you would have felt.

'The headmaster tried to persuade my dad. "Mr Austin, she's only a child." But it made no difference. I never went out to work. My dad kept me at home to help my mother because she had to have a serious operation.'

Elsie and May's memories create a grim picture of life in the Victorian and Edwardian school system for working-class pupils. Fifty in a class; forms and benches raked or sloped; no visits or trips; no extra-curricular activities; lessons in silence (except for sewing); physical punishment (especially for boys); boys down one side of the classroom, girls down the other and never the twain.... Imagine that. No talking! Boys and girls not allowed to sit together!

Aunt May described to me a system whereby children were grouped not by age, but by 'standards'. She remembers being moved from standard four to standard five early. The bright children were moved up to the next grade early. The not-so-clever children were made to repeat the year.

'I remember the headmaster stood at the classroom door,' she said. 'There were usually five of us in our class who always went up two or three weeks before we should, because we'd learned all we could at that grade. So it was always the same names that got called out. Well, he came in this day and took all the others but not me.

'And all the other children behind me started to gossip. Really catty. "Eh! She's not going up this time." I felt awful. And all at once the door opened. He called out: "May Austin." He had my name down all the time, but he'd forgotten to call it out. Oh, I felt like a queen when I was going out of the classroom.'

Work was done in complete silence. It consisted mainly of listening and copying. 'They used to chalk most of the things on the blackboard. You had to copy them down,' said Gran. The curriculum was mostly reading, writing and arithmetic and there were no practical lessons in Aunt May's school. Gran described a nature lesson about hedgerows, but it never occurred to the teacher to take the pupils out to look at a real hedgerow.

'It was a nature lesson,' said Gran. 'If I remember rightly it was "The Hedgerows". You know, the berries and the trees and the hedgerows. And it was a nature lesson where you just sat down, you worked at your desks, and you listened.'

Physical punishment was the norm. It was rare for girls to be caned, but Aunt May remembers having to watch as her brother was brutally struck in front of her eyes.

'They had the cane hanging down at the front of the classroom. I never got it. But your Uncle Ernie did. I don't know what it was for. He wasn't in my class, but he came into my classroom, I don't know why. He put out his hand and the teacher brought the cane down on it. "And the other hand," said the teacher. "And the backs."

'And the teacher pulled his hand out again and said: "You might as well have the half dozen." Ernie was crying. It was real cruel.'

Aunt May remembers being in serious trouble with her father for allowing a girl to copy from her.

'I remember one day we did this examination paper. It was dictation. And there was a girl next to me. Her name was Alice Leather and she couldn't spell. I used to let her copy, you know and all at once the teacher said: "May Austin, stop that!" She could see what I was doing.

'Alice used to bring me things for letting her copy. I went home one day and my dad pointed to what I was holding and said "Where did you get that?"

'I said, "Alice Leather's given it me." I was only twelve.

"What for?" he said.

"Letting her copy," I said.

'He said, "Well, you can take it back!" I nearly got a good hiding. I had to give it back. Well, I felt sorry for her because she couldn't spell.'

Talking about spelling, Aunt May also remembered the school inspector's visiting.

'The inspector used to come and ask questions. He'd stand at the bottom of the room. And then he'd say, "Who can spell MISSISSIPPI?" And I put my hand up. "Go on," he said.

'I remember taking a deep breath and saying very fast, "M... I... double... S... I... double... S... I... double... P... I." And there seemed to be a sort of silence, you know.

'And he said, "Say it again, slowly." So I did.'

In those days stories were as powerful as they are today and always have been since the very beginning of human existence. Even at the age of ninety-six, Aunt May recounts stories which had an effect upon her as a small child. Books had a powerful effect as well and became lasting treasures, in spite of (or perhaps because of) their limited supply.

'We didn't have many books. I had one book: *Five Weeks in a Balloon*. I still have it. I won a Bible at Sunday School. I still have that,' Aunt May told me.

As I left them that evening with my tape-recorder tucked under one arm, I thought of an old African proverb which says: 'When an elderly person dies, it is as if a whole library has gone up in flames.' I realised then that my Gran and Aunt May were both libraries — and I had just joined.

Steve Austin

Remember the fifth of November

Please to remember
The fifth of November,
Gunpowder, treason and plot.
I see no reason
Why gunpowder treason
Should ever be forgot.

Why is it that as soon as the pumpkins of Hallowe'en have been thrown in the bin, our thoughts immediately turn to sparklers, fireworks and bonfire night?

What is so special about the fifth of November?

Who exactly are people talking about when they're sitting next to a bundle of rags made to look like a person, and asking for 'a penny for the Guy'?

The real Guy was Guy Fawkes, a Yorkshire Catholic who lived in the time of King James I of England, who reigned from 1603 until 1625. Guy Fawkes was the man who, in 1605, *would* have ignited the barrels of gunpowder piled up under the Houses of Parliament and blown up not just the Houses of Parliament, but the King, his son Henry, lots of lords and nobles and almost all of the ministers in the Privy Council. Imagine someone today planting a bomb to blow up the Royal family and all the government, including the prime minister! Luckily, Guy Fawkes was stopped in time, but how did he come to be there in the first place?

Although Guy Fawkes was the first man to be caught in the gunpowder plot, he didn't actually think it up himself. The man who had the initial idea was Robert Catesby, a Catholic like Guy Fawkes. At this time in England it was particularly difficult for Catholics. Queen Elizabeth I, who reigned just before James, had introduced laws making it a crime to go to mass, to try to convert anyone to the Catholic religion, or even to shelter a priest. If you were caught you had to pay a heavy fine, or worse still, go to prison. Catesby thought that this persecution was unjust and in 1603 began to dream up a scheme that would dispose of, in one go, all those who opposed the Catholic faith. From this idea there followed a whole web of secrets, lies, forgery, spies, betrayal, torture and death.

Catesby's idea was fairly simple. He was to rent a room in the Houses of Parliament and dig a tunnel until he was under the room that the King and all his men would be in – the Lord's Chamber. Once under the chamber, he would pile up as much gunpowder as he could lay his hands on and blow the whole lot sky high. This was to be done on the day when the King was due to open the Houses of Parliament. The opening ceremony was always performed in the same room and he was sure to have enough powder to make the plot a success and kill the King.

Clearly, with a long tunnel to dig and a lot of gunpowder to buy and hide, Catesby needed help. By May 1604, Catesby had persuaded four others to help him and sign an oath of secrecy. Arrangements were made about renting storage rooms and buying the necessary materials, but the costs were getting higher and higher and more people, including Guy Fawkes himself, had to be brought in to help finance the operation. It is difficult to say exactly how many conspirators there were because most of the documents of the time were either forged, lost or mysteriously destroyed. Some of the people involved may in fact have been spies in the pay of the violently anti-Catholic Secretary of State and chief adviser to the King, Robert Cecil, the arch-enemy of the plotters and the man out to catch them all.

The tunnelling actually began in December 1604. After six months of digging, something actually happened. They found that there was already a room under the Lords' Chamber. Unbelievably, a coal merchant who had rented the room was moving out and it would be available to anyone who could afford the rent. Either they were being lured into a trap, or they had been extraordinarily lucky. The plotters moved in immediately.

They began to prepare the room, but in March 1605, about six months before the big day, some of the plotters began to have doubts. Catesby himself, the man who had thought up the original plan, was feeling guilty about all the innocent people that would be killed along with the King, and went to talk to a priest, Father Garnet, about it. He didn't tell Father Garnet the whole plot, but did drop enough hints to make him suspicious. Being a Catholic priest, Father Garnet didn't want to tell the King of what he suspected, but he did write to the Pope asking him to forbid the plotters (or anyone else) from using force against the Protestants. The Pope refused. Later, Father Garnet heard the whole plot while listening to a confession, but because anything heard in the confessional is held sacred and must be kept between the confessor, the priest and God, he could not tell anyone what he knew.

By the autumn, the number of people involved in the plot had grown still further and of course, as the number got higher, so did the risk of being found out. Some of the conspirators were as worried as Catesby about killing innocent people including some Catholic lords and others who would be sympathetic to their cause. Then a mysterious letter arrived at the house of Lord Monteagle who was married to the sister of one of the conspirators, Francis Tresham. The letter warned him to stay away from the Houses of Parliament on the fifth of November. He showed the letter straight to Robert Cecil.

Catesby, however, was unaware of this and the plot pressed ahead as planned. Guy Fawkes was to light the fuse, while Catesby and the others went north to try and raise a small army of Catholics who would be ready to move down to London when chaos followed the explosion.

Guy Fawkes took over the watch at the cellar under the Lords' Chamber at 10 o'clock on the night of the fourth of November. The King wasn't due to arrive for hours and Fawkes had a long night ahead. He paced about nervously, waiting in the dark, but he never got to light his bonfire. On the stroke of midnight, Robert Cecil sent his men to arrest Guy Fawkes. The plotters had been betrayed and Fawkes was heavily out-numbered and had no chance of escape.

After his arrest, the King said that Fawkes should be 'gently' tortured, but Fawkes was a stubborn man and refused to give up any information. It took four days and many different tortures, including being stretched on the rack, before he finally gave in, and even then, he did not give everything away.

However, all his bravery counted for nothing because within a week of his arrest all the other conspirators except one were either dead or captured. Robert Catesby was among those killed, probably on the orders of Robert Cecil.

On the twenty-sixth of January, the few plotters who were still alive were brought to trial. But it wasn't a trial as we would recognise it today; it was merely for show. Everyone knew that they would be found guilty. They did not even have a chance to defend themselves. The punishment was severe, for they were not only to be executed, but they were to be dragged, or drawn to their place of execution by horse, then hanged, but cut down while still alive to suffer further until they finally died.

You might think that this was the end of the matter. But the evil Cecil wanted to put the blame for the plot on the Catholic priests who had known about it, so that he could press the King into being ever more severe against the Catholics. Poor Father Garnet was made out to be the man who thought the whole plot up and was also executed.

So the next time you pass a few stuffed rags on the street, or wave your sparklers, or watch fireworks light up the sky, or stare into the flames of a bonfire, remember what the 'fifth of November' was really about and spare a thought, if not a penny, for poor old Guy.

Trevor Gorin

Children of winter

'Hush,' said Dan suddenly. 'Listen.'

They all stopped.

Rap. Rap. Rap. Knuckles on wood. The children froze into silence.

Again: Rap. Rap. Rap.

''Tis the messenger!' Dan shouted, and ran to pull back the door.

A man was standing there, half-leaning against the door, and as it opened he slumped down in the doorway. He rolled a little way to the side and settled down on to the snow, as if to sleep.

''Tis Clem!' said Dan.

Catherine slammed the door shut again and stood with her back to it. Dan and Tessa were slow to grasp what had happened. They tried to pull her away so that they could open up the door again.

'Catherine. Bring him in. 'Tis Clem.'

'I daren't,' she said.

'But Cathy!' Dan tried to heave her away. 'He's my friend.'

'Tha saw his face,' said Catherine.

'He's sick.'

'Then tha *must* let him in,' pleaded Tessa.

'Doesn't tha understand!' Catherine refused to be pulled away.

''Tis thee as doesn't understand!' said Dan. 'He's Clem. He lives here. He's sick, Catherine. Let him in.'

'Think! If he is sick, then he may have the plague.'

Tessa understood at last. 'But we can't just leave him there, Cathy.'

'What else can we do?' The question was hopeless. 'What would Mother do?'

'Tha knows very well what Mother would do,' said Dan indignantly. 'She'd bring him in and give him a good supper, an' look after him till he was better, even if she didn't know him.'

Catherine sighed. If only it was as simple as that. 'Well, is the broth still warm?'

Tessa could have hugged her sister. 'It soon can be. The fire won't be out yet; I can bring up the heat again. Shall I do it now?'

Catherine nodded and stood back to let her pull the door open. 'Keep away from Clem, though,' she whispered. She held on to Dan's hand firmly.

Clem was standing up now. In the sharp light of the moon they could see how bright his eyes were, and how his face was blistered with sweat. He didn't even seem to notice Tessa as she moved in front of him to the fire to rekindle its flame under the cooking-pot.

Dan would have run to him all right. 'Clem,' he said. The man looked at him but didn't seem to know him.

'I came back here to be alone,' he said. 'I don't know what to do with myself.' He staggered down on to his knees, too weak to stay standing.

Catherine had seen sick sheep do this. It was all she could do to stop herself from running forward to catch him. She knew that was what her mother would have done. She'd have kept him warm, and fed him, of course she would, but she would also have kept him away from the children. Would she really have sent them away from home and made them face out a winter in a cold barn if she'd known that something like this would happen? She must do what her mother would do, then.

She pulled Dan back into the barn with her. 'He'll be all right, Dan,' she said firmly. 'Stay here now.' She brought out her own rug from the straw and laid it over Clem.

'The broth is ready,' called Tessa.

'Bring it in the small bowl,' said Catherine. 'Put it down by him.'

Tessa brought the steaming bowl over carefully. 'Here Clem,' she said, putting the bowl near his face where he could smell the thick soup. ''Tis hot, mind, and good for thee.'

To Catherine's relief Clem managed to raise himself up so that he was leaning on one elbow. He pulled himself against the side of the barn, where he could sit comfortably, and sipped greedily at the broth.

''Tis good,' he said thickly. 'Bless thee for this.'

'Come in, now,' said Catherine to Tessa. 'We must talk. Leave him to finish that.'

They went back into the barn and closed the door behind them. Catherine was almost too wrapped up in worry to speak. If only there was something to tell her what she must do now. Without realising it she had sat herself down on the thinking-log and had picked up the slate, and was drawing letters on it absently. Dan and Tessa sat down with her and watched her quietly. Their father would be like this, lost in thought, before he spoke to his family of his problems. They must wait, then.

'I want to help Clem,' she said at last. 'And yet I want to do what Mother wanted, and save us all. Save thee.'

They said nothing; Dan because he didn't understand, and Tessa because the problem was too big.

'If we bring Clem in here, and he does have the plague, then we may catch it, too. We may die of it.'

'We needn't touch him, though,' said Tessa. 'He could lie over there, away from us.'

'But we'd be breathing the air he breathes,' insisted Catherine. She shuddered, remembering what Maggie Hoggs had said to them. 'I don't know what spreads the plague from one person to another, but I do know that when he sneezes he puts

it into the air. We mustn't ever go that close to him. I won't let thee.'

'So what do we do? We can't leave him out there. I think we should risk it, and make him better.' Tessa jumped up. 'Come on, Cath. Let's do that.'

'I know what we can do,' said Dan, but Catherine ignored him. She ran to the door before Tessa could reach it.

'Clem,' she called. 'Can tha hear me?'

'Aye,' he said, and his voice sounded much stronger now.

'Has tha been down to the village?'

'I have. I went down there to see our Moll.'

'Did tha see anyone – did tha see the people at Tebbutt's farm?'

Clem coughed. The three children were kneeling down behind the door, straining to catch his voice. 'I saw no one. Doors and shutters closed. No one on the streets. No one in the fields. No voices – nobody, nothing. I thought I were sleeping. I've never come on owt like that before. I went on down to our Moll's house, and tha knows what Moll's like – she's one for singing, she is.'

Catherine nodded. Molly Carter, Clem's sister, was their mother's friend, a big, rosy woman with a loud voice; a bit noisy at times, her mother used to say; the sort of person you couldn't be doing with first thing in the morning.

'Well, there wasn't a sound coming from her house when I got there. And those children of hers, like a herd of fresh goats, shouting and banging and climbing up me as I was a tree in a field – not a sign of them. I went in, thinking to find a feast ready, because there's always food at Moll's house. Table were set, mind, and I sat meself down to tuck in, thinking they were gone to market or some such. Why – milk was blue in cup. Bread were stale as stones. And then I heard our Moll, upstairs, crying.'

He started coughing and sneezing again. Tessa fetched the candle over from the table-stone, so its light would give them some comfort.

'What happened, Clem?' prompted Catherine.

'Our Moll was alone in the house, and she was alone because those three children of hers were all dead, and her husband was out digging the ground for a place to put them in. I went to comfort her, and she screamed at me to get away from her, and save myself at least. It was too late for her, she said. She locked herself into her room and I knew she was right. I gave her my blessing and grabbed my bits and pieces from the table and ran for my life out of the village. I never want to go back down there again. And then, yesterday it may have been, I started with this fever. Maybe I can shake it off, I thought, if I get to shelter in the barn. But how was I to know there'd be three children here?'

His words sank away from them. The children sat for a long time in their crouched positions by the door. What Clem had told them, then, was the thing that their mother had dreaded above everything else, and that she'd done so much to avoid. He had brought the plague from their village to the barn.

Berlie Doherty

Dinosaur discovery

Storm after storm after storm. It seems as if the planet is so unsure of itself. But then again this is a time when all is in turmoil.

Today is the fourth day of storm – the hail pelts the green fern leaves, the lightning stings the tall cycad trees and the continuous rain softens the underbelly of the soil until it becomes as soggy as damp bread. The rocks slacken their grip on the topsoil. Day and night the earth cowers; night and day the sky cracks its whip.

Where the land rises, just beyond the great lake, two young velociraptors, the swiftest of thieves, scream in terror as the walls of a moving mountain trap them in a muddy gully. A favourite feeding ground, the male and female velociraptors knew little of the movements of the soft soil and the brittle mountain sides. This is where they would meet their doom. A massive lightning bolt struck the volcano; a direct hit that split the mountain in two forcing the two halves apart. Great rivers of yellow and gold lava oozed from within and the stench of poisonous gases filled the air.

The velociraptors could only howl and scream in terror as the mountain walls edged nearer and their clawed feet plunged deep into the moving mud mouth that opened like an oven door to swallow their bodies.

There they perished and there they lay, those big, bizarre, but beautiful beasts, for millions of years until one day, another dinosaur (this one yellow and mechanical, but just as hungry) hacks out the fossilised bones of the two animals.

The find excites the world. Never before have the remains of a dinosaur been found in such good condition. Even the hides of the beasts have been preserved.

After analysis a palaeontologist makes a statement to the press: 'Two rare creatures, velociraptors, from the same family group – possibly even brother and sister – were found in a clay pit in East Sussex. They are remarkably well preserved and they are the first to be discovered in this part of Europe. It is indeed a very important find.'

'You say they may have been brother and sister? How did they meet their doom? Were they fighting?' A string of questions pour upon the scientists. A television sound man pushes the boom mike closer.

'No. They were not fighting. Oddly enough it may have been just the opposite. You see their claws were intertwined, as if... well as if they were protecting each other.'

John Rice

Carrie's war

He threw up all over Miss Fazackerly's skirt. He had been feeling sick ever since they left the main junction and climbed into the jogging, jolting little train for the last lap of their journey, but the sudden whistle had finished him.

Such a noise – it seemed to split the sky open. 'Enough to frighten the dead,' Miss Fazackerly said, mopping her skirt and Nick's face with her handkerchief. He lay back limp as a rag and let her do it, the way he always let people do things for him, not lifting a finger. 'Poor lamb,' Miss Fazackerly said, but Carrie looked stern.

'It's all his own fault. He's been stuffing his face ever since we left London. Greedy pig. *Dustbin.*'

He had not only eaten his own packed lunch – sandwiches and cold sausages and bananas – but most of Carrie's as well. She had let him have it to comfort him because he minded leaving home and their mother more than she did. Or had looked as if he minded more. She thought now that it was just one of his acts, put on to get sympathy. Sympathy and chocolate! He had had all her chocolate, too! 'I knew he'd be sick,' she said smugly.

'Might have warned me then, mightn't you?' Miss Fazackerly said. Not unkindly, she was one of the kindest teachers in school, but Carrie wanted to cry suddenly. If she had been Nick she would have cried, or at least put on a hurt face. Being

Carrie she stared crossly out of the carriage window at the big mountain on the far side of the valley. It was brown and purple on the top and green lower down; streaked with silver trickles of water and dotted with sheep.

Sheep and mountains. 'Oh it'll be such fun,' their mother had said when she kissed them good-bye at the station. 'Living in the country instead of the stuffy old city. You'll love it, you see if you don't!' As if Hitler had arranged this old war for their benefit, just so that Carrie and Nick could be sent away in a train with gas masks slung over their shoulders and their names on cards round their necks. Labelled like parcels – Caroline Wendy Willow and Nicholas Peter Willow – only with no address to be sent to. None of them, not even the teachers, knew where they were going. 'That's part of the adventure,' Carrie's mother had said, and not just to cheer them up: it was her nature to look on the bright side. If she found herself in Hell, Carrie thought now, she'd just say, 'Well, at least we'll be *warm*.'

Thinking of her mother, always making the best of things (or pretending to: when the train began to move she had stopped smiling), Carrie nearly did cry. There was a lump like a pill stuck in her throat. She swallowed hard and pulled faces.

The train was slowing. 'Here we are,' Miss Fazackerly said. 'Collect your things, don't leave anything.

Take care of Nick, Carrie.'

Carrie scowled. She loved Nick, loved him so much sometimes that it gave her a pain, but she hated to be told to do something she was going to do anyway. And she was bored with Nick at the moment. That dying-duck look as he struggled to get his case down from the rack! 'Leave it to me, silly baby,' she said, jumping up on the seat. Dust flew and he screwed up his face. 'You're making me sneeze,' he complained. 'Don't *bounce*, Carrie.'

They all seemed to have more luggage than when they had started. Suitcases that had once been quite light now felt as if they were weighed down with stones. And got heavier as they left the small station and straggled down a steep, cinder path. Carrie had Nick's case as well as her own and a carrier bag with a broken string handle. She tucked it under one arm, but it kept slipping backwards and her gas mask banged her knee as she walked.

'Someone help Caroline, please,' Miss Fazackerly cried, rushing up and down the line of children like a sheep dog. Someone did – Carrie felt the carrier bag go from under her arm, then one suitcase.

It was a bigger boy. Carrie blushed, but he wasn't a Senior: he wore a cap like all the boys under sixteen, and although he was tall, he didn't look very much older than she was. She glanced sideways and said, 'Thank you *so* much,' in a grown-up voice like her mother's.

He grinned shyly back. He had steel-rimmed spectacles, a few spots on his chin. He said, 'Well, I suppose this is what they call our ultimate destination. Not much of a place, is it?'

They were off the cinder track now, walking down a hilly street where small, dark houses opened straight on to the pavement. There was sun on the mountain above them, but the town was in shadow; the air struck chill on their cheeks and smelled dusty.

'Bound to be dirty,' Carrie said. 'A coal-mining town.'

'I didn't mean dirt. Just that it's not big enough to have a good public library.'

It seemed a funny thing to bother about at the moment. Carrie said, 'The first place was bigger. Where we stopped at the junction.' She peered at his label and read his name. Albert Sandwich. She said, 'If you came earlier on in the alphabet you could have stayed there. You only just missed it, they divided us after the R's. Do your friends call you Ally, or Bert?'

'I don't care for my name to be abbreviated,' he said. 'Nor do I like being called Jam, or Jelly, or even Peanut Butter.'

He spoke firmly but Carrie thought he looked anxious.

'I hadn't thought of sandwiches,' she said. 'Only of the town Sandwich in Kent, because my granny lives there. Though my dad says she'll have to move now in case the Germans land on the coast.' She thought of the Germans landing and her grandmother running away with her things on a cart like a refugee in a newspaper picture. She gave a loud, silly laugh and said, 'If they did, my gran 'ud give them What For. She's not frightened of anyone. I bet she could even stop Hitler. Go up on her roof and pour boiling oil down!'

Albert looked at her, frowning. 'I doubt if that would be very helpful. Old people aren't much use in a war. Like kids – best out of the way.'

His grave tone made Carrie feel foolish. She wanted to say it was only a joke, about boiling oil, but they had arrived at a building with several steps leading up and told to get into single file so that their names could be checked at the door. Nick was waiting there, holding Miss Fazackerly's hand. She said, 'There you are, darling. There she is, didn't I tell you?' And to Carrie, 'Don't lose him again!'

She ticked them off on her list, saying aloud, 'Two Willows, one Sandwich.'

Nick clung to Carrie's sleeve as they went through the door into a long, dark room with pointed windows. It was crowded and noisy. Someone said to Carrie, 'Would you like a cup of tea, bach? And a bit of cake, now?' She was a cheerful, plump woman with a sing-song Welsh voice. Carrie shook her head; she felt cake would choke her. 'Stand by there, then,' the woman said. 'There by the wall with the others, and someone will choose you.'

Carrie looked round, bewildered, and saw Albert Sandwich. She whispered, 'What's happening?' and he said, 'A kind of cattle auction, it seems.'

He sounded calmly disgusted. He gave Carrie her suitcase, then marched to the end of the hall, sat down on his own, and took a book out of his pocket.

Carrie wished she could do that. Sit down and read as if nothing else mattered. But she had already begun to feel ill with shame at the fear that no one would choose her, the way she always felt when they picked teams at school. Suppose she was left to the last! She dragged Nick into the line of waiting children and stood, eyes on the ground, hardly daring to breathe. When someone called out, 'A nice little girl for Mrs Davies, now,' she felt she would suffocate. She looked up but unfocused her eyes so that passing faces blurred and swam in front of her.

Nick's hand tightened in hers. She looked at his white face and the traces of sick round his mouth and wanted to shake him. No one would take home a boy who looked like that, so pale and delicate. They would think he was bound to get ill and be a trouble to them. She said in a low, fierce voice, 'Why don't you smile and look nice,' and he blinked with surprise, looking so small and so sweet that she softened. She said, 'Oh it's all right, I'm not cross. I won't leave you.'

Minutes passed, feeling like hours. Children left the line and were taken away. Only unwanted ones left, Carrie thought. She and Nick, and a few tough-looking boys, and an ugly girl with a squint who had two little sisters. And Albert Sandwich who was still sitting quietly on his suitcase, reading his book and taking no notice. *He* didn't care! Carrie tossed her head and hummed under her breath to show she didn't either.

Someone had stopped in front of her. Someone said, 'Surely you can take two, Miss Evans?'

'Two girls, perhaps. Not a boy and a girl, I'm afraid. I've only one room,

see, and my brother's particular.

Particular about what, Carrie wondered. But Miss Evans looked nice; a little like a red squirrel Carrie had once seen, peering round a tree in a park. Reddish brown hair and bright, button eyes, and a shy, quivering look.

Carrie said, 'Nick sleeps in my room at home because he has bad dreams sometimes. I always look after him and he's no trouble at all.'

Miss Evans looked doubtful. 'Well, I don't know what my brother will say. Perhaps I can chance it.' She smiled at Carrie. 'There's pretty eyes you have, girl! Like green glass!'

Carrie smiled back. People didn't often notice her when Nick was around. *His* eyes were dark blue, like their mother's. She said, 'Oh, Nick's the pretty one, really.'

Miss Evans walked fast. She was a little woman, not much taller than Carrie, but she seemed strong as a railway porter, carrying their cases as if they weighed nothing. Out of the hall down the street. They stopped outside a grocery shop with the name SAMUEL ISAAC EVANS above the door and Miss Evans took a key from her bag. She said, 'There's a back way and you'll use that, of course, but we'll go through the front for the once, as my brother's not here.'

The shop was dim and smelled mustily pleasant. Candles and tarred kindling, and spices, Carrie thought, wrinkling her nose. A door at the back led into a small room with a huge desk almost filling it. 'My brother's office,' Miss Evans said in a hushed voice and hurried them through into a narrow, dark hall with closed doors and a stair rising up. It was darker here than the shop and there was a strong smell of polish.

Polished linoleum, a shining, glass sea, with rugs scattered like islands. Not a speck of dust anywhere. Miss Evans looked down at their feet. 'Better change into your slippers before we go up to your bedroom.'

'Haven't got any,' Carrie said. She meant to explain that there hadn't been room in their cases but before she could speak Miss Evans turned bright red and said quickly, 'Oh I'm sorry, how silly of me, why should you? Never mind, as long as you're careful and tread on the drugget.'

A strip of white cloth covered the middle of the stair carpet. They trod on this as they climbed; looking back from the top, Carrie saw the marks of their rubber-soled shoes and felt guilty, though it wasn't her fault. Nick whispered, 'She thinks we're poor children, too poor to have slippers,' and giggled.

Carrie supposed he was right. Nick was good at guessing what people were thinking. But she didn't feel like giggling; everywhere was so tidy and clean it made her despair. She thought she would never dare touch anything in this house in case she left marks. She wouldn't dare *breathe* – even her breath might be dirty!

Miss Evans was looking at Nick. 'What did you say, dear?' she asked, but didn't wait for an answer. 'Here's the bathroom,' she said – proudly, it seemed. 'Hot and cold running water, *and* a flush toilet. And your room, just by here.'

It was a small room with two narrow beds and a hooked rug between them. A wardrobe and a wicker chair and a large, framed notice on the wall. The black letters said, The Eye Of the Lord Is Upon You.

Miss Evans saw Carrie looking at this. She said, 'My brother is very strong Chapel. So you'll have to be especially good Sundays. No games or books, see? Except the Bible, of course.'

The children stared at her. She smiled shyly. 'It may not be what you're used to but it's better to get things straight from the start, isn't it? Mr Evans is a good man, but strict. Manners and tidiness and keeping things clean. He says dirt and sloppy habits are an insult to the Lord. So you will be good, won't you? You look like good children.'

It was almost as if she were pleading with them. Asking them to be good so that *she* wouldn't get into trouble. Carrie was sorry for her, though she felt very uncomfortable. Neither she nor Nick were particularly tidy; at home, in their warm, muddly house, no one had expected them to be. Milly their maid, always picked up their toys and made their beds and put their clothes away. Carrie said, 'We'll try to be good, Miss Evans.'

'Call me Auntie,' Miss Evans said. 'Auntie Louise. Or Auntie Lou, if that's easier. But you'd best call my brother Mr Evans. You see, he's a Councillor.' She paused and then went on in the same proud tone she had used when she showed them the bathroom, 'Mr Evans is a very important man. He's at a Council meeting just now. I think I'd best give you your supper before he comes back, hadn't I?'

Nina Bawden

JUST IMAGINE!

The old man who sneezed

There was an old man
who sneezed and sneezed.
He sneezed and sneezed:
  A-A-TISHOO!
  AH-AH-AH-AH-
  AH-AH-AH-AH-
  TISH-OOO!
Just like that!
He sneezed till his eyes were wet. He sneezed till his ears popped. He sneezed so long and he sneezed so loud: he sneezed till his nose blew off.
  AH-AH-TISHOO!
The old man's nose blew off and away. It shot out of the door, into the street and over the road. It just missed a bus. It just missed a car. It only just missed a lorry!

Across the road went that old man's nose. Over a pavement, through a front door, down a passage, and right into a kitchen where a dear old lady was eating her breakfast, and it fell into that old lady's cornflakes! There it lay, the old man's nose, all among the crispy yellow cornflakes!

It made the old lady jump. 'Dear me, dear me,' the old lady said. 'How did that nose get there?'

And she put on her glasses and looked again: 'What a *big* nose! What a *red* nose. It looks just like the nose that belongs to the old man over the road,' that old lady said.

Now the old man who sneezed was very upset when his nose blew away. He wanted to sneeze again. 'I can't sneeze without my nose,' he said.

So he began to chase it.

He ran out of the door into the street, but *he* was careful. He let a bus go by. He let a car go by. He let a lorry go by. He looked both ways and didn't try to cross the road until it was absolutely clear, even though he wanted to sneeze very badly.

He managed to AH-
He could AH-AH.
But he really couldn't Tishoo!
But when the road was safe he ran over the road to the old lady's house.

But he didn't run through her front door. He was a very polite old man. Even though he wanted to sneeze he wouldn't go in without being asked. Because he was polite he waited on the old lady's step. He knocked on the old lady's door. He rang the old lady's bell. He rattled the old lady's letter-box.

'Have you got my nose in there?' he called.

'Come in, come in,' said the dear old lady. 'I've got your nose here – it's perfectly safe. It fell in my cornflakes and wasn't hurt a bit. I'll put it back on for you if you like,' the old lady said.

So the old man went into the old lady's kitchen and she put his nose back on for him.

'There!' she said. 'That won't come off in a hurry. But how did you come to lose it?'

'I sneezed it off,' the old man said.

'And I very much want to sneeze again, only I'm afraid it will blow off. I have very strong sneezes,' the old man said.

'Yes my dear,' said the old lady. 'I see what you did – you forgot to be polite. You were polite about not coming into my house without knocking first, but you weren't polite about sneezing. YOU DIDN'T USE A HANDKERCHIEF. No wonder your nose blew off.'

She went to her cupboard and got him three paper ones.

'Hold those to your nose when you sneeze,' she said. 'You'll be as right as rain.'

So the old man held the three paper handkerchiefs to his nose. Then he sneezed and sneezed:

'A-A-TISHOO!
AH-AH, AH-AH,
AH-AH, AH-AH,
TISHOO!'

He sneezed so loud he made the old lady jump. He sneezed so loud that her door-bell rang by itself, her knocker knocked by itself, her letter-box rattled by itself. All the buses in the road stopped. The cars stopped. The lorries stopped.

'AH-AH, AH-AH,
AH-AH, AH-AH,
TISH-ISH-ISH-ISH-ISHOO!'

That was the biggest sneeze of all!

But because he held the handkerchiefs close to his face the old man's nose stayed on. Even though he sneezed again:

'ATISHOO, ATISHOO.'

And then again (not so loud): 'ah-tishoo.'

Then quieter still: 'ah-tishoo.'

And then so quiet only he could hear it: '...!'

But his nose stayed where it belonged. And it never came off again, for he always remembered to be polite and to look for a handkerchief before he sneezed:

'AH-AH-AH-AH-TISHOO!'

Now the old lady can eat her breakfast, and the traffic can go up and down the road without anyone having to worry about that old man's nose!

Dorothy Edwards

Hank Prank and the adenoids

Hank Prank wasn't Hank Prank's real name; Hank Prank's real name was Henry Bradley Lawes. But his mother and father called him Hank Prank and so did everyone else because Henry Bradley Lawes was always playing tricks and making jokes. When his mother said, 'Henry, do you want a hamburger?' he'd answer, 'I've never tasted a jamburger.' Whenever Henry made a joke like that his mother would raise her eyebrows, roll her eyes, sigh deeply, and say, 'Oh, Hank Prank!'

One day, when Hank had said 'potdogs' for 'hotdogs' and 'schmurtle' for 'turtle' and 'yucky' for 'lucky', Mrs Lawes turned to her husband and said, 'Honey, I'm worried about Hank. I don't think he hears very well.'

'He hears what he wants to,' answered Hank's father, looking over the top of his newspaper.

'He's changed nearly every word I said to him today.'

'That's his idea of a joke,' said Mr Lawes. 'That's why we call him Hank Prank.'

'All the same, I'm going to take him to the doctor to have his ears checked.'

The next morning Hank's mother made an appointment with the doctor. When they arrived at his office, the doctor said to Hank, 'Hallo Henry. I'm Dr Levy.'

'Dr Sleevy?'

'No, Dr Levy.'

'Dr Gravy?'

Hank's mother raised her eyebrows, rolled her eyes, sighed deeply, and muttered, 'Oh, Hank Prank!'

Dr Levy examined Hank's throat, looked into his ears with a little light, and then gave him a hearing test. He took Hank into a small soundproof room, sat him in a swivel chair, and put real earphones on him. Hank liked that part. Then Dr Levy went out and spoke into a microphone outside the room. He told Hank to raise his hand whenever he heard a sound. Dr Levy and Hank could see each other through a window. Hank listened carefully for the sounds coming through the earphones, but he didn't hear many, and his hand usually stayed in his lap. After the hearing test Dr Levy called Hank out and said to him, 'Well, your mother's right, Hank. You do have a hearing problem.'

'I have a steering problem? I'm not even old enough to drive!'

'You have a *hearing* problem, but we can cure it easily. You'll have to go to the hospital to have your adenoids out.'

'I have to have my Dad in a doubt? Doubt about what?'

'No, no, Hank, adenoids. ADENOIDS! They're little lumps at the back of the throat, and yours are a bit sore. When you have them out, you'll be able to hear again.'

'I'm not allowed to drink beer now,' Hank answered solemnly.

His mother and the doctor raised their eyebrows, rolled their eyes, sighed deeply, and together said, 'Oh, Hank Prank!'

The hospital was in a city two hours away from where Hank and his family lived. Early one morning the Lawes family got up, had breakfast, and packed the car. With Mum and Dad in the front seat, and Hank and his sister Henrietta in the back, they left their home town and drove through the countryside towards the city. Henrietta fell asleep before they were out of town, but the rest of them were wide awake. Hank's mother said from the front seat, 'Oh Hank, look at the billy goat.'

'I don't see any silly boat,' Hank answered.

Hank's mother sighed. A little later she pointed out the window and said, 'Oh Hank, look at the pig farm.'

Hank looked around and said, 'A wigwam? There aren't any Indians around here, are there?' His father rolled his eyes. When they were almost at the hospital Hank's mother said, 'Look at that big dog.'

'What's a pig hog?' asked Hank. His father and mother looked at each other and didn't say anything for a long time. Hank's father gripped the steering wheel tighter and muttered to himself. Finally, as they pulled into the driveway of the hospital, his father said very slowly and very quietly, 'That operation had better work.'

Inside the hospital they took the lift to the children's ward. A young woman came out from behind a counter in the middle of the corridor and said, 'Hallo, I'm your nurse.'

Hank answered, 'You're not supposed to curse.'

'Oh, you must be here for the adenoid operation,' she went on. 'It's being done by Dr Jones.'

'By Dr Bones!' said Hank in a surprised voice. 'What kind of a name is *that* for a doctor!'

'I'll take you to your room.'

'I don't want a broom. I'm not going to sweep this place up. I'm here for an operation, you know.'

His parents looked at each other a very long time, shook their heads sadly, and followed the nurse and Hank into the room. Hank's mother slept beside him in the room that night on a cot which the nurse brought in. He had a nice supper, but the next morning he was given no breakfast. The nurse told him that this was because today was the day he was going to have his operation. Soon after he got up, Hank's door opened and his father walked in. He sat on the bed and talked to Hank about hikes that the four of them were going to take when Hank was out of the hospital and back home, and he held Hank's hand. Then the door opened. A man wearing a white coat stepped inside.

'Hallo, I'm Dr Jones.'

'Hallo, Dr Bones. I'm Hank Prank.'

'Hallo, Mr Spank. I'm Dr Bones.'

'No, you're not. I am.'

Dr Jones looked at Hank for a long time. 'I think I see the way this conversation is going. Roll up your sleeve please.'

Hank answered, 'I don't have to sneeze.'

'Your SLEEVE, Hank, your SLEEVE.'

'Oh, my sleeve. What about my sleeve?'

'ROLL IT UP, PLEASE.'

'Oh, roll it up. Why didn't you say so?'

By this time Dr Jones had reached down and rolled up Hank's sleeve himself. 'Now, I'm going to give you a little needle,' he said.

'A little tweedle?'

'Right, Hank. Here's your tweedle.' And he stuck the tweedle in Hank's left arm.

'Ow!' said Hank. 'That makes me very... very... uh... sleepy.' He felt his eyes s-l-o-w-l-y closing.

Hank soon became sleepier and sleepier. He half remembered being lifted out of his bed and being put on a bed with wheels. He remembered riding on the bed down the hall, being pushed by another nurse with his father walking beside him and holding his hand. He didn't remember the operation at all. He thought he had a dream that he was in a room with doctors and nurses. One of them had put a little handkerchief over his mouth and nose. In the dream the handkerchief person said, 'Now count to ten, Henry.' Somebody with his voice counted, 'One... two... three... four... snore....' He could remember no more.

When Hank woke up he was back in his own room in the hospital. His mother and father were both sitting on the bed next to him, and his father was holding his hand. Hank looked at him and then fell back to sleep.

When he woke up the next time, his parents were sitting in chairs beside the bed, and Henrietta was doing a puzzle on the floor. Hank's mother smiled at him. 'HOW DO YOU FEEL, HANK?' she asked.

Why are you shouting?' asked Hank.

'THE OPERATION'S OVER, HANK,' said his father.

'Why are you two yelling?' asked Hank.

Then his father and mother looked at each other and smiled. The operation had worked. Hank could hear well again.

Hank smiled. Then he drifted back to sleep.

The next day the Lawes family left the hospital and drove back to their home. Hank sat in the back seat with a blanket across his lap to keep him warm. Henrietta slept again. After a while, Mrs Lawes looked out the window and said, 'Look at that big dog.'

Hank looked and answered, 'Yes, it is a big dog.' Hank's mother smiled.

A little later Hank's father pointed and said, 'Hank, look at that pig farm.' Hank looked and replied, 'They sure have a lot of pigs there.' Hank's father smiled.

As they got closer to home, both parents spoke at the same time, 'Hank, look at the billy goat.'

Hank waited a moment. Then he answered, 'I don't see a silly boat!'

His parents looked at each other. Neither of them said a word. His father slowly stopped the car beside the road. They looked back at Hank. Their expressions were worried. But Hank had a big, silly grin on his face. 'Fooled ya!' he said.

They looked at each other and laughed. Together they shook their heads, rolled their eyes, and sighed, 'Oh, Hank Prank.'

Jules Older

The peanut butter princess

There was once a large palace with fine gardens. In the palace lived a Prince and a Princess. They were very happy most of the time and the Princess liked to have peanut butter on toast for breakfast.

A wide path led from the large, brown front door of the palace, past gaily coloured flower beds, past goldfish ponds full of fat goldfish whose tails flashed in the sunlight, past neatly clipped bushes, across smooth green lawns, all the way to a large iron gate, tall and black.

The gate was the only way out of the palace grounds. It opened on to the path to the village, a long winding path that led through the darkness of the Wild Wood.

The Wild Wood was where the Dragon lived.

The Dragon had short stumpy legs that weren't very good for walking or running. He had beautiful wings, but was far too lazy to stretch them out and fly. So in order to get about the dragon drove a steamroller. Now you might think that a steamroller is a funny sort of vehicle for a dragon to drive. You might think it's a funny sort of vehicle for anyone to drive, but the Dragon thought his steamroller was perfect. You see, he didn't need to buy coal to fire the boiler, he didn't even need to collect wood to fire the boiler. All he had to do was puff his dragon-fire into the fire box and the steamroller would be ready to go. So a steamroller really is a sensible vehicle for a dragon to drive. At least that is what the Dragon thought. He also thought it was perfect for catching the Prince and, for some reason we don't know, this is what the Dragon most wanted to do. He would sit on his steamroller, in the Wild Wood, and wait for the Prince to come out of the palace.

Every morning the day would start in the same way. The Prince would have a dish of royal shredded oats and the Princess would have a large plate-full of toast and peanut butter. The Prince didn't like peanut butter and had tried to persuade the Princess to have marmalade on toast or strawberry jam on toast, but all she would eat for breakfast was peanut butter on toast.

One morning the Princess took the peanut butter jar from the shelf and let out a little scream. The Prince came running to see what was the matter.

'There's no peanut butter,' gasped the Princess. 'The jar is empty.' She looked at the Prince.

'You must go down to the village, this very moment,' she cried, 'and get me a new jar.'

Then she stamped her foot very hard and looked terribly angry. So the Prince set out across the palace gardens, past the flower beds, past the goldfish ponds, past the neatly clipped bushes, across the smooth green lawns up to the large iron gate.

He began to walk towards the village. It didn't take the Prince long to get there. He went into the village shop and bought a jar of peanut butter. Then he started back up the path towards the palace.

He was about halfway to the palace when he heard a loud clanking noise coming from behind the trees that lined the edge of the path. He began to walk more quickly, but the noise was getting closer. The noise became very loud and the Prince looked behind him. Coming out of the Wild Wood, in a cloud of red and white smoke, he saw a large steamroller driven by the Dragon. The Prince was very frightened. The Dragon puffed out a large puff of dragon fire. He was going to catch the Prince.

Luckily, the Prince was very fit. He did a lot of running and he began to run now. He clutched the jar of peanut butter and ran as hard as he could. Because steamrollers are quite slow the Prince was able to run to the gate before the Dragon could catch him. He ran safely into the palace grounds, very much out of breath.

When he gave the Princess the peanut butter she began to spread it thickly on her toast. She didn't want to hear how the Prince had just managed to escape from the Dragon.

For a while everything in the palace returned to normal. Outside the palace grounds the Dragon waited in the Wild Wood. He sat on his steamroller and waited for the Prince to come out of the gate again. While he was waiting a salesman came to visit him.

'Steamrollers are very slow,' said the salesman. 'Why don't you buy one of these?'

He showed the Dragon a super-twin motor bike.

The Dragon had never seen a motor bike so the salesman showed him how it worked. After he had taken the motor bike for a short ride the Dragon was sure it was better than a steamroller. The salesman agreed to take the steamroller in part exchange and the Dragon bought the super-twin motor bike.

For a week the Dragon practised riding his new motor bike and then he felt he was ready. So the Dragon waited in the Wild Wood. He sat on his motor bike and waited for the Prince to come out of the palace gate.

Soon after this the Prince and Princess were sitting down to breakfast. The Princess picked up the jar of peanut butter and found that it was empty again.

'Oh no!' she cried. 'You must go right now to get some more peanut butter for me.'

The Prince knew that if he went out into the Wild Wood again the Dragon would try to catch him. He also knew that he could run faster than the steamroller so he wasn't very afraid. The Prince walked out of the palace, past the flower beds, past the goldfish ponds, past the bushes and over the green grass to the tall iron gate.

He looked around carefully. The Wild Wood looked empty and all was quiet. Cautiously the Prince slipped out on to the path. He walked quickly. All the way to the village he kept looking over his shoulder, but the Dragon didn't come. In the village shop the Prince bought an extra large jar of peanut butter and started on his way home, walking as fast as he could.

The Prince was about half way back to the palace when he heard a noise from behind the trees that lined the edge of the path. He looked behind him. The Dragon was coming out of the Wild Wood — on a motor bike!

The Prince started to run, but he knew it would be no good. Even he couldn't run faster than a super-twin motor bike. Behind him the Prince could hear the deep throbbing of the motor bike engine, getting closer and closer. What could he do? He was going to be caught by the Dragon. Then the Prince had a wonderful idea. He stopped running and turned to face the Dragon. He unscrewed the top of the peanut butter jar and scooped out a handful of the contents. He spread the peanut butter on the road where the Dragon would come and then turned to run, as fast as he could, towards the palace gate. As he ran he heard a screech of brakes and then a crash. The Dragon had skidded on the peanut butter and fallen off his motor bike. By the time the Dragon had picked up his motor bike the Prince was safe inside the palace grounds.

The Prince took the jar of peanut butter to the Princess. She didn't care that he had nearly been caught by the Dragon again. She just snatched the jar from his hands. The Princess was about to spread the peanut butter when she stopped and turned to the Prince with a look of disgust on her face.

'Ugh!' she said. 'This jar has been opened and it's only half full. That's no good. You will have to go back and get me a full jar. You must go right now!'

The Prince stared at the Princess for a moment, then he smiled.

'No,' he said. 'You go, this time.'

The Princess was gone for about half an hour. When she returned she said, in a small voice, 'Please, may I have marmalade on toast for breakfast this morning?'

And, as far as I know, she has been eating marmalade on toast ever since.

Robin Mellor

Green marmalade to you

There was once a boy called Clutha who lived with a cat and a crocodile and they were very happy together. The strange thing was that each of them spoke a different language from the other two so that ordinary conversation was full of guesses and question marks. However, mostly they understood each other very well.

One day they all got up together and each one of them opened his bedroom door at exactly the same time as the other two.

'Good morning,' said Clutha.

'Gone mooning,' said the cat.

'Green marmalade!' cried the crocodile.

(But they all meant the same thing really.)

'It's a lovely day, isn't it?' called Clutha.

'It's a lively doe, isn't it?' observed the cat.

'Ladylike Ding-Dong!' exclaimed the crocodile, putting up its blue frilly sunshade to prove it.

(But, as you will have guessed they all meant the same thing really.)

Now the problem was to find something they all liked for breakfast. Clutha wanted porridge, and the cat said he wanted chops (though he may have meant chips.) As for the crocodile, it couldn't choose between cheese and cherries so they decided to have something totally different.

'How about bacon and eggs?' asked Clutha. 'Very tasty bacon and eggs!'

'Break-in and exit! Very toasty!' agreed the cat.

'Broken explosions. Very twisty!' the crocodile concurred twirling its blue sunshade.

So they had broken explosions for breakfast and they enjoyed them very much. But after breakfast there is always a problem, as you know. Dirty dishes!

'We'd better do the washing up, I suppose,' said Clutha.

'We'd batter down the swishing cup,' nodded the cat.

'Buttered clown is wishing out,' finished the crocodile – or it sounded like that.

So they did the dishes and then they went out to play.

Now, maybe one green marmalade you'll wake up on a ladylike ding-dong and have broken explosions for breakfast too – you'll find them very twisty! But don't forget to butter the clown and swish the cup when you do the wishing out, will you?

Margaret Mahy

Dragon in Class 4

'Now then,' said Miss Green, 'while our brains are fresh this lovely autumn morning, spelling! We'll have all our old tricky friends.' Sam saw a sharp golden snout poke through the beech leaves and two blackberry-bright eyes looked at him through the rosehips. One of them winked. 'Try your hardest, Sam. If you get just one right, I'll be pleased with you. I'll say each word twice.'

Sam sighed. You can say them ten times, he thought, and I'll still get them wrong. It's not *saying* them that helps, it's *seeing* them.

'They,' began Miss Green. She put her tongue between her teeth. '*They.*'

Sam looked at her sadly. Inside Miss Green's head were the right spellings, but he couldn't see inside Miss Green's head. Then, an extraordinary thing happened. A speech bubble came out of Miss Green's lips. She brushed her hand across her lips as though she were brushing away a hair.

The bubble floated over to Sam. It had little black tadpoles swimming in it. The tadpoles caught hold of each other's tails and turned into fat black letters. There was a *t*, an *h*, an *e* and a *y*. The bubble burst and the fat black letters fell down on to Sam's paper. No one else noticed anything. The *e* was a great show-off, it kept turning somersaults to attract attention. Sam laughed. Miss Green looked up. At once the letters lay down flat, the *t* first, then the *h*, *e* third and *y* last. They shrivelled and vanished. Sam wrote down *they* and made a very black, thick *e* in the middle.

'Was,' went on Miss Green, '*was.*'

Another bubble blew out from her lips, blue as the sky. She flicked it away, and it floated over to Sam and burst into shining stars. The stars ran together into glittering letters, a *w* and an *a* and an *s*, and settled gently on Sam's page. The *w* lay still, but the *a* and the *s* rolled about as though it were a great joke to be in *was* at all. Sam put his hand over them to keep them still and felt them tickle, like a shrimp he had once caught at the seaside. When he took his hand away, they vanished. He wrote down *was* with an *a*, and an *s*.

'Down,' continued Miss Green. '*Down.*'

An aeroplane zoomed out of her mouth, dropped four letters by parachute and exploded. The letters touched down on the head of the girl in front. They formed up and began to march down her pigtails in single file. 'There's a fly on my hair,' said the girl, shaking them off, but not before Sam had noticed their marching order, and seen that the *w* came before the *n*.

'Talk,' Miss Green was saying, '*talk.* You should all get that right. You do enough of it!'

Out of her mouth came a yellow post office van. It sped over to Sam's desk, flung out four little red telephones and hurtled away. The telephones untangled their flexes, which turned into little red letters, a *t* and an *a* and an *l* and a *k*, and all four began to ring each other up and talk in tiny crackling voices.

'Ssh!' said Miss Green, looking over at Sam.

'Ssh!' said Sam to the telephones. They stopped talking and vanished. Where they had been, Sam wrote down *talk* with an *al* in the middle.

So it went on. It was the first spelling test Sam had ever enjoyed. It wasn't easy, though. The letters had so much bounce and character. The word 'jump' came out as four splendid showjumpers, and even when the horses turned into letters they still went on jumping. The *m* with its three legs was particularly good. Sam had to put his ruler across them to keep them still. But he remembered to put the *m* in '*jump*'.

'And now,' said Miss Green, 'just for fun and to end with, elephant! *Elephant!*'

This'll be fun, thought Sam, to see an elephant come out of Miss Green's mouth. But nothing came out of Miss Green's mouth. No speech bubble, nothing! Sam was aghast. He looked at the nature table. Not a leaf moved. He looked round the room.

Through the archway, in the bay where the big playthings were kept, a baby elephant was putting on a pink top hat with the letters *e l e* in silver on the front. Beside it crouched the little dragon busily tying a broad pink ribbon round its middle. The ribbon had a big *ph* on it in silver. The dragon gave the baby elephant a little push to turn it round and fixed the pink bow on the end of its tail with three letters hanging from it. Sam laughed. Fancy great big enormous *elephant* ending in tiny, little *ant*! He wrote it down. When he looked again the bay was empty.

'Papers in,' called Miss Green, 'and everyone have a rest.'

Phew! thought Sam, what a lesson! He felt suddenly hungry. Good job I've got my banana.

'Sam,' cried Miss Green. 'Wonderful boy! You have got every one right! A great big, enormous clap for Sam, everybody!'

Sam stood by Miss Green's desk staring at his spelling paper with the red ticks going all down the page and the gold star shining at the bottom. Generous Class 4 clapped like mad and he knew he was grinning like an idiot. He looked hard at the nature table, but it held only leaves and berries and branches. He raised his eyes to the window and saw far away on the other side of the playing field a baby elephant in a top hat and a small dragon walking together under the golden autumn trees. The dragon seemed to be offering the elephant a banana.

June Counsel

The wonderful washing machine

Mrs Lenska filled up the washing machine with water and when she went to put the clothes in she stared in amazement. 'Come here, Henry,' she called to Mr Lenska. 'Come and see what's happened to the washing machine.'

Mr Lenska had a good look. 'It seems to be full of strawberry jam,' he said at last. 'Mm – smells like strawberry jam, too, *tastes* like strawberry jam. It *is* strawberry jam.' He looked sternly at Mrs Lenska. 'What have you been doing?' he demanded.

'Nothing,' she returned, 'except fill it up with water. I don't know how it happened.'

'I expect it was those kids from the next apartment,' Mr Lenska said. 'They're always up to some trick or other.'

'It couldn't be them,' Mrs Lenska said. 'They're away at summer camp. Besides, I haven't opened the door to anyone all morning.'

'Well, what are we going to do about it?' asked Mr Lenska. 'It's perfectly good jam, but we can't eat that much.'

'We'll keep a few pounds of it,' Mrs Lenska decided, 'and put the rest down the waste disposal. There's nothing else we can do.'

So they cleared out the jam and then they cleaned out the washing machine with fresh water, and it was soon working perfectly again. All went well for a few weeks, and then Mrs Lenska noticed something wrong again.

'Henry,' she said, 'the washing machine's gone peculiar again.'

Mr Lenska groaned. 'Not more strawberry jam?' he said.

'No,' she replied. 'This time it seems to be chocolate sauce.'

'That's not possible,' said Mr Lenska.

'Possible or not,' Mrs Lenska retorted, 'that's what it is. Taste it and see.' He tasted it, and it was.

'This is ridiculous,' he said, 'but I'm due in town in an hour's time. I can't stay to help you clean it out this time, but I'll call in and ask the engineer to come and take a look at it.'

When the engineer arrived he said it certainly was chocolate sauce, but he didn't seem too surprised. 'Would you mind telling me,' he asked Mrs Lenska, 'where you bought this machine?'

'I exchanged it for my mahogany table,' she told him.

'With Mrs Kalman downstairs?'

'That's right – how did you know?'

'I've been called to this machine before,' he replied. 'It's had at least five owners to my knowledge. Nobody seems to know what to do with it when it starts behaving like this.'

Mrs Lenska was annoyed. 'I think Mrs Kalman might have warned me,' she said. 'After all, my mahogany table doesn't do peculiar things.' She glared at the engineer. 'Can you fix it?' she asked.

'Well, I'll have a look at it,' he said, 'but I don't hold out much hope of being able to alter it. Most of the time it works normally, and then something seems to change it altogether.' He smiled sadly. 'I think it must be magic,' he added.

'Magic!' snapped Mrs Lenska scornfully. 'There never was any such thing.'

'Of course not,' murmured the engineer.

He checked all the valves and all the switches; he tried out the motor; he looked at the joints connecting the water to the machine; he even read the instructions on the washing powder packet; but he could find nothing wrong at all.

'That settles it,' said Mrs Lenska. 'I shall just have to buy a new one. I was saving for something else, but this is more important.'

'Are you sure,' asked the engineer, 'that you can't find a use for this one?'

'Quite sure,' she replied. 'What on earth could I do with all that strawberry jam and chocolate sauce?'

The engineer shook his head. 'What does Mr Lenska think about it?' he enquired.

'Henry thinks exactly as I do,' was the answer. 'He thinks it's a nuisance and a bad bargain.'

'In that case,' said the engineer, 'I'll tell you what I'll do. I'll ask around. There may be somebody who'd know what to do with it.'

'Do that,' said Mrs Lenska.

A few weeks later the engineer called again. 'Did you buy a new washing machine?' he asked.

'Yes,' said Mrs Lenska, 'and I haven't had a single problem with it. I can't think why I put up with the other one for so long.'

'Have you still got the old one?' asked the engineer.

'Yes,' she said. 'Have you found someone to take it off my hands?'

'I think so, if you will take a portable TV for it. Mrs Slinger in the next block is willing to do a deal. She says your old washing machine is exactly what she has been looking for.'

Mrs Lenska said, 'Henry, go with the man and take a look at Mrs Slinger's portable TV. If it's okay we'll let her have the old washing machine for it.'

An hour later the deal was fixed. Mrs Lenska did her washing and watched TV at the same time. She never gave her old washing machine a second thought.

In the next apartment block Mrs Slinger was watching the washing machine with great interest. 'I do believe it's vegetable soup!' she cried. 'Delicious!' and she and Mr Slinger and the little Slingers had vegetable soup for lunch. When they had finished there was still a lot left. 'Go and knock all the doors in the block,' she said, 'and tell them there's free soup at the Slingers'. Tell them to bring their own basins.'

In no time at all the soup had been gladly received and all that remained to be done was rinse out the washing machine with hot water. After that the machine worked normally for quite a long time, which was a good thing, because Mr and Mrs Slinger had a lot of children and a lot of washing to do, but every once in a while it produced something special – custard, or lemonade, or broth, or ice-cream, and always Mrs Slinger shared it out among her neighbours. It never once occurred to her to throw the surplus away.

The engineer called one day. 'How are you getting on with the washing machine?' he enquired.

'Fine!' said Mrs Slinger, and explained what was happening and how she was dealing with it.

I'm glad of that,' said the engineer. 'I always knew that one day, sooner or later, somebody would know what to do with it.'

Linda Allen

The chocolate touch

John had the bad habit of chewing things when he was thinking hard. This morning he had several things to think about. What had made the toothpaste taste like chocolate? What had made the orange juice taste like chocolate? What had made the bacon and eggs taste like chocolate? What had made the toast and butter and marmalade taste like chocolate?

Each one of these things had felt the way it had always felt before. The toothpaste had been soft and pasty. The bacon had been hot, crisp and oily. The toast had been crunchy and the marmalade sticky and lumpy. But everything had tasted like the chocolate he had eaten in bed last night.

John put a gloved thumb in his mouth and thoughtfully chewed. His mother had frequently pointed out to him that chewing his gloves made little holes that let in the cold air. But he chewed them just the same when he was thinking hard. This time he noticed something very queer about the thumb of his glove. Instead of tasting leathery, it tasted like chocolate. John pulled his thumb out of his mouth. The part of the glove that had been in his mouth was now brown, instead of black like the rest.

He bit the end of the leather thumb again. It came right off in his mouth, leaving his own thumb bare. John chewed, and it was like chewing leather made of chocolate, leather that melted like chocolate.... In a second or two he swallowed it.

The gloves were not new. John had had them quite a while. He couldn't understand why he had never thought of eating them before. He tried to tear off one of the fingers, but the leather was too strong for him. He put it into his mouth, and it immediately turned into chocolate. Then he was able to break it off easily. He popped it into his mouth and chewed it up and swallowed it. It was delicious.

Walking along devouring his glove, John did not notice one of his schoolfellows, Spider Wilson, until he heard his voice. 'John's gone crazy! John's gone crazy!' Spider yelled. Then he turned on John. 'Don't they feed you where you live?' He sneered. Spider was in the class above John's and was one of the meanest and slyest boys in the whole school.

John gulped down a large piece of the second glove's palm and looked pleased.

'What's the matter?' Spider demanded. 'Do your parents make you eat leather?'

'This is special leather,' John replied. He licked his lips and sighed contentedly. 'It turns into chocolate as soon as you put it into your mouth. Look.' John bit off the glove's little finger and took it out of his mouth.

'Now it's chocolate.' He put it back into his mouth and gulped it down.

'Give me a piece,' Spider said.

'Why should I?' John wanted to know. 'They're my gloves.'

'Hand over a piece,' Spider said.

'Do I eat your gloves?' John asked reasonably, his mouth full of chocolate. 'Why should you eat mine?'

'Those aren't real gloves,' Spider said. 'Whenever one person has sweets, he has to share them with the others. That's the club rule.'

'What club?' John asked.

'Never mind what club,' Spider said. 'But you'd better let me have some of that chocolate.'

Without waiting longer, Spider snatched what was left of the second glove. John was too surprised to resist, and he didn't want to, anyhow. He had a feeling that he'd had enough chocolate for a while. He was getting a bit thirsty.

Spider ran only a little way ahead. When he saw that John wasn't going to fight to get the glove back, he started to eat his prize. He stuffed the leather into his mouth and took a big bite. Spider stopped short in his tracks. He frowned and bit deep into the leather again. Disgusting! It tasted worse than just leather. It tasted like leather with which a boy had made mud pies and snowballs and patted old dogs.

John thought perhaps he might be getting late for school, so he started running. He left Spider Wilson spitting the soggy remains of the glove into the gutter.

Still giggling to himself about the

defeat of the enemy, John walked between the great stone pillars at the entrance to the school grounds. He had gone no more than halfway to the main building when he heard Susan Buttercup calling him. She was standing near the jungle gym with some of her friends.

'I've got something to show you, John,' she shouted.

As she came running to meet him, he could see that she was waving something in her hand that flashed as it caught the rays of the sun. It was an old silver coin. 'It's a birthday present!' she explained, showing him the coin. 'Isn't it beautiful?'

The sight of such wealth made John forget the triumphs of his own day. 'It's a good present,' he said. 'Are you sure it's made of silver, though? I once got a whole bag of gold coins in a Christmas stocking, only they were chocolate coins covered with gold paper.'

'Of course it's real, silly,' Susan said. 'My daddy said so. You can feel it if you don't believe me.' She handed him the coin.

John looked at the coin suspiciously.

'All right,' Susan said. 'Bite it, if you think it isn't real. Go on, bite it!'

John felt rather silly. 'I can see it's real now,' he said. 'I don't have to bite it.'

'But I want you to,' Susan insisted. 'You weren't sure. Well, *make* sure. That's what they always do on television. When a cowboy wants to make sure a coin's real, he bites it.'

John put the coin about halfway into his mouth and reluctantly bit it. His teeth went right through the coin. The part that had passed between his lips was hard but sweet chocolate.

Susan could hardly believe her eyes. She had given John a complete circle of silver. He sadly handed back a crescent.

John didn't know what to say. Susan couldn't speak. Tears trickled down her cheeks like rain down a windowpane. She looked at the piece of coin in her hand. She looked up at John, whose face was red with embarrassment. 'John Midas,' Susan blurted out at last, 'I hate you.' She turned and ran away before John could think of anything at all to say.

Patrick Skene Catling

The saver

Philip came down with a bump. He let go of the kite and it flew just a little way to a narrow gap between two rocks. It settled between the rocks and the long dragon tail curled itself round and round in a neat pile by its side.

The little cloud that had led them safely all through the long journey now sat bouncing on one of the rocks. As it bounced, it changed from black to white and grew thinner and thinner. With a faint sigh, it disappeared, leaving only a damp mark on the rock.

Philip suddenly felt very lonely. The cloud had gone, the kite was very still as if it was deeply asleep, and the robin was nowhere to be seen. He stood up and looked around. He was in a clearing in the forest. Which way should he go? He didn't want to end up lost. There might be wild animals.

He had come so far across the sea that he might be in a land where lions or tigers lived. On the other hand, he couldn't just stay here. He made up his mind to be brave and started walking towards the trees.

Just where the path went into the forest, the robin flew down from the top of a bush and landed on Philip's shoulder. The robin's happy song helped to make the forest seem a little less gloomy. Even so, Philip shivered a little. The crooked branches creaked and the shiny, wet roots of the trees reminded him of the octopus he had seen in the sea. The forest echoed with the strange tick-tock music of water drops as they tumbled down from the dark leaves on to the trembling ferns.

The path grew narrower and brambles tried to pull him back. As the forest became darker, the robin stopped singing. He pressed himself against the side of Philip's neck and Philip could feel the little heart beating fast.

They came to a rushing stream with stepping stones across it. Philip had just jumped from the last stone on to the path at the other side when he felt a rumbling in the ground. The robin squeaked and flew into the bushes. The air grew colder and there was the thunder of galloping hooves.

Without knowing why, Philip dived into the ferns and lay hidden under some bushes as the noise grew louder. The ground shook and pounded and big chunks of earth flew through the leaves and branches. He pressed his face to the damp soil and held his breath. The noise stopped. Whoever, or whatever, it was, had halted on the path next to where he was hiding. There was absolute silence for a moment, then a growling sound.

Philip twisted his head and looked up through the ferns. Two huge black horses towered above him. The riders were dressed in red robes. They had their backs to him but he knew from the horrible noises they made that they were not men. They were sniffing the air like dogs and then growling to each other. They turned and Philip saw green eyes, black hairy faces, wolf-like, snouts and pointed yellow teeth. They sniffed and started to look down towards him as if they had caught his scent.

He heard a flutter of wings and he saw a blur of red fly past him towards the riders. It was the robin. The bird darted and dived just out of reach of the snapping jaws, then landed on the head of one of the horses. Philip's chest grew tight as the rider raised a hairy claw and brought it crashing down towards the robin. At the last second, the little bird flew off and the claw hit the horse's neck. The poor beast snorted and reared into the horse in front. The two riders tumbled backwards but managed to hang on to their horses as they charged towards the stream. The horses leaped the

water and Philip stood up to watch as they thundered away down the path with their riders' red robes flying in the wind.

As soon as they were out of sight, Philip ran in the opposite direction. He tripped and stumbled over broken branches on the path and his feet sometimes slid into the huge hoof-prints that the horses had left. He kept running until he could run no further. He sat down on some moss at the side of the path and listened. There was no thunder of hooves, only the drip-dropping of the water from the trees.

The robin flew down and landed on Philip's knee. He let Philip reach out and stroke the feathers on the top of his head.

'Thank you for saving me. You were very brave,' Philip said.

The robin whistled and sang and bobbed so hard that Philip had to smile even though he was still out of breath and rather scared.

'We'd better not stay here, robin. Those horrible things on horses might be back looking for us. Is it far to the end of the forest?'

The robin bobbed and shook his head. He jumped on to Philip's shoulder as he got up and started along the path. The trees were becoming less dense and the light was less gloomy. Streaks of sunlight were shining down through the leaves. Philip was just beginning to feel happy that he could see the end of the forest when he heard a strange noise. It was coming from beyond the trees – somewhere out in the sunshine. He moved closer and listened again. Someone with a most extraordinary voice was singing a song.

Philip peered from behind a tree and gasped with amazement. The singer was a small beaver who was flying back and forth on a tiny swing that hung from the lowest branch of an apple tree. A little way behind this tree, there was a cosy-looking cottage. The front door was open and a delicious smell of baking bread floated to Philip on the breeze.

The small beaver started his song again and swung up and down so hard that the whole tree rocked. A ripe apple tumbled from the top of the tree, bounced off the lowest branch, and hit the beaver on the shoulder. The shock made him let go of the swing and he toppled backwards off the seat. He managed to catch hold of the rope with his foot but he suddenly found himself swinging upside down with his nose an inch above the ground.

'Help, help, I'm falling in,' he shouted.

Philip was just about to dash to the rescue when a large badger rushed out of the cottage, almost tripping over her apron. She was carrying some knitting and, in her speed, she had forgotten about the ball of wool which came rolling behind her out of the front door.

'Now don't make a fuss, Baby B. I warned you about swinging too hard,' she said, dropping the knitting and trying to catch hold of the swing.

'Help,' shouted Baby B and grabbed her apron as he swung past.

The sudden jerk pulled the badger off balance and she fell over. Baby B waited until the swing came level with her again then kicked his foot free from the rope. He sailed through the air and crashed on to the poor badger's tummy, knocking all the wind out of her with a tremendous 'OOUUFFF!'

'Thank you, Mrs Badger,' said Baby B, sliding to the ground. 'You stopped me from getting hurted.'

'Oooh,' gasped Mrs Badger as she sat up slowly, trying to get her breath back. 'Really, Baby B, you do get yourself in some pickles.'

'It wasn't a pickle, it was an apple. It bonked me on the shoulder and I let go and then I was falling in.'

'You weren't falling in, Baby B. You might have fallen off and you nearly fell down but there was nothing for you to fall in.'

'I might fall in my head,' said the small beaver.

'On, Baby B, on. You can't fall in your head.'

'A flea could.'

'Now that's enough of your nonsense,' Mrs Badger said, as she got to her feet. 'Oh dear me, oh dear me – look at my knitting. All the stitches are off.'

She picked up the needles and started to slide the stitches back on.

'Oh dear me, Mrs Badger, it's all over the garden,' said Baby B. 'I'll help you. I'm good at helping.'

He ran over to the ball of wool and picked it out of a rose bush. He started to roll it up as fast as he could but it got caught round his leg and the more he tried to get himself free, the more he got tangled up. He turned one way, then the other, and then ran round in circles until he began to look more like a ball of wool than a beaver.

'Help, Mrs Badger, it's trying to knit me.'

Mrs Badger groaned, tucked her knitting into her apron pocket, and patiently began to unwind Baby B. She had just got him free and was about to roll the wool into a proper ball when she saw Philip peering from behind the tree. Her eyes grew wide as he walked towards her.

''Are you... are you one of the witch's men?' she asked in a scared, gruff voice.

'I don't think so,' said Philip, 'but I did come here by magic. On a kite, all the way from my home. Under a cloud. And a robin came to meet me and....'

'A cloud? A robin?' interrupted the badger. 'You mean, you're the...?'

'The saver?' broke in the little beaver. 'It's the saver! Hooray! Hallo, Mr Saver. I can help you. I'm good at helping and I'm not scared...'

Nigel Hinton

The boy who stole the rainbow

Ali Kasim was the water boy at the palace of the Amir of Patanagar. Patanagar was a desert kingdom and the ruler was the third richest man in the world. There was nothing which he saw and wanted that he could not buy, but no sooner was it his than he lost all interest and sent it down to his deep cellars where all his treasures were stored, and there it would lie, ignored and forgotten.

Ali Kasim spent every day of his young life, from the rising of the fiery sun in the East to its setting in the blood red West, trudging across the blistering desert sands to the royal well where he would draw water, fill his earthenware pot, then wearily trudge back to the palace kitchens where he would pour the precious contents into what seemed like bottomless vessels.

Rain rarely fell on Patanagar, and when it did, it always fell at night, so, of course, no one had ever seen a rainbow. But Ali Kasim had. One day, when he was very young, he had accompanied his father to the well. His father had drawn a bucket of water, and as he was pouring it into the waterpot, the sun's rays reflected the most beautiful rainbow that Ali had ever seen. It shimmered between bucket and pot for just a moment, and as the last drop of water was poured, it seemed to vanish into the waterpot. Ali had got so excited that he overturned the pot searching for the rainbow. When he saw his son's eyes, gleaming in wonder, his father laughed, and explained the secret of the rainbow to the young boy. After his father died, Ali had taken over the job of water carrier, and he would often pretend to catch a rainbow in his waterpot, but he knew that such a beautiful thing could not ever belong to one person, except for a brief moment.

The Amir had one daughter named Princess Farrah. On cool evenings Ali would see her in the courtyard. The princess loved colourful clothes; ruby-red chiffon from China; orange organdie from Odemis in Turkey; saffron yellow taffeta from Tunisia; gorgeous green brocade from Barcelona, in far away Spain; beautiful blue velvet from Venice, and indigo and violet damask from distant, exotic lands across the sea. Farrah's laugh was like the sparkle of clear water and her smile as radiant as the sun. Ali would often gaze at her secretly as she lit up the dull courtyard for a brief moment, but then she would silently slip back into the palace, vanishing like all his secret rainbows.

And so, the years slipped by. Ali grew into a tall, handsome young man and Princess Farrah grew more radiant with each passing day. Rich young princes from distant lands, hearing of her beauty, travelled to the palace hoping to win her hand in marriage, but the princess had long ago lost her heart to the handsome young water carrier whom she often saw crossing the palace courtyard. Sometimes she would wave to him shyly from some distant window and he would nod or smile at her, but he knew that she could never be anything more than a magical rainbow to him; a rainbow, captured within a palace.

One day the lonely princess could bear it no longer. Tearfully, she went to her father.

'Father,' she whispered. 'There is something I want, but I cannot have.'

'Cannot have! Cannot have!' spluttered the Amir in astonishment. 'My dear child; there is nothing on this Earth that you cannot have! Just tell me what it is and it shall be yours!'

Prince Farrah shook her head sadly. 'But father,' she sobbed, 'when I tell you what I want more than anything in the world, you will change your mind and say I cannot have it.'

The Amir could not bear to see his daughter so unhappy. 'Have I ever broken a single promise that I made

to you?' he cried.

Princess Farrah again shook her head. 'But if I ask you,' she whispered timidly, 'will you really keep your promise? No matter what it is I ask for?'

'My child,' replied the Amir, 'all my life I have got everything I ever wanted; but more than anything else I have always wanted you to be happy, and I will pay any price for that, so no matter what you ask for, it shall be yours.'

Princess Farrah gazed into her father's eyes. 'Father,' she said, slowly, 'I want to marry Ali, the water carrier.'

For a moment the Amir was shocked into silence, but he was a man of his word, and a promise made must be a promise kept, but he knew that in keeping this promise he would lose his precious rainbow. 'But you, my daughter, are a princess. You are my greatest treasure; you are my rainbow. You must marry a prince and live in this palace forever. If you were to marry a water carrier, what would become of you?'

'But father,' smiled the princess. 'I need not marry a water carrier. You could easily make him a prince!'

The Amir nodded. 'And if I allowed you to marry him, you would remain in the palace forever?'

'Yes, father,' promised Princess Farrah.

'Then, we must think of a plan. My people would not think well of me if I made him into a prince without good reason.'

Two days later, for the first time that anyone could remember, the rain fell on Patanagar in the afternoon. The Amir, Princess Farrah and all the courtiers crowded into the yard to feel the coolness of the rain – and then the most wondrous rainbow appeared in the sky. It stretched across the entire kingdom and everyone reached out towards it, gasping in amazement.

'I want the rainbow!' cried the Amir. 'I want the rainbow for my palace and I will pay any price for it!'

Ali had been sheltering in the courtyard but when he heard the Amir's words he boldly stepped forward. 'Your Highness,' he said, bowing, 'if you are willing to pay any price to own the rainbow, I am willing to steal it for you!'

'As these people are my witnesses, I will pay any price!' cried the Amir.

'Then watch carefully,' warned Ali, 'for I know the secret of the rainbow, but as I gather it in to my water pot, it will disappear from the sky and no one will ever see it again.'

Without another word, Ali was gone. Every face turned towards the rainbow, and then a gasp went up from the crowd. Before their very eyes the red and orange, the yellow and green, the blue, indigo and violet seemed to be dissolving. The brilliant colours began to fade and melt away,

and within a very short time the glorious rainbow was gone without a trace, and all they could see was a blue, cloudless sky.

Soon Ali returned, clutching his water jar which was tightly sealed. A rousing cheer went up from the crowd.

'Let us see the rainbow! Let us see the rainbow!' they cried with one voice.

Ali hugged the jar close to him. 'You cannot see the rainbow,' he explained. 'It is safe in the jar, but if I open it, then it will immediately escape and be lost forever. This jar belongs to His Highness, the Amir!'

Smiling proudly, the Amir accepted the earthenware pot. 'And now, young man, name your reward!' he exclaimed, joyfully.

Lowering his eyes meekly, Ali spoke in a soft voice. 'I wish you to make me into a prince!'

The crowd gasped, but clutching his water pot, the Amir replied in a loud voice. 'I made this young man a promise, and a promise cannot be broken. I hereby declare you to be the Prince of Patanagar.'

The crowd cheered.

'Is that all you wish as payment for this precious rainbow?' asked the Amir.

'Your highness,' replied Ali. 'Now that I am a prince, I would beg for your daughter's hand in marriage!'

The crowd gasped in amazement.

'It is perfectly in order for a prince to seek my daughter's hand in marriage!' proclaimed the Amir, 'and if she should accept this young prince then tomorrow there shall be a grand Royal Wedding.'

Princess Farrah, as radiant as the rainbow which had so recently attracted everyone's attention, stepped forward, smiling, and taking Ali's hand, said, 'I gladly accept your offer.'

The crowd cheered even louder than before. Still clutching his pot, the Amir turned to his daughter with a beaming smile and gave her a knowing wink. Princess Farrah returned the wink, happy in the knowledge that he still had his treasured rainbow, but even happier that he had learned how to share it with someone else, because, after all, isn't that what rainbows are for?

Al Moir

Time spinner

I was alone in my BedCube. Lying on the bed with my eyes shut. Imagining I was alive in Elizabethan times; back in the 1990s. Bicycle-riding, skateboarding, swimming – it must have been great to have been an Elizabethan.

'Rosemary!' Mum's voice boomed from the corridor. 'We're off now!'

I don't know why she sounded so excited. Dad was only taking her to the Wilkinses at number 4023 for a SupaDisk SoftWare Party. Yawn. Bore. All they do at these SoftWare parties is to sit around and swap one old DigiTuneDisk for another even older DigiTuneDisk. They all sound the same anyway. Yawn. Bore.

I carried on imagining. This is what I imagined. I was bent over the steering handle of a bright red Elizabethan bicycle, racing hard down a steep, steep hill. Trees and buildings flashed past me in a whirl of colour and the wind whined and whistled through my ears.

'Have you gone deaf or something?' Mum was standing over me. Hands on hips.

'Eh?'

'I've been calling you for the last five minutes.'

Now Dad was on the scene.

'She spends too much time lying around moping, if you ask me,' he said.

I *didn't* ask you, I thought.

'I don't mope,' I said.

'Well, I don't know what else you'd call it.'

I don't suppose you would, I thought.

'Imagining,' I said.

'Imagining has no useful function for anyone. You're old enough to know that by now.'

Why does everything have to be *useful*? I thought.

'We won't be late back, love.' Mum's turn.

'Oh...?'

She gave me one of her quizzical looks. Did I sound too disappointed? Did

she suspect what I had in mind?

'What homework have you got tonight?'

'Elementary astronomy and technology.'

'Now, you *will* finish it before going to bed?'

'Of course, Mum.' My eyes smiled sweetly, but my fingers were tightly crossed behind my back; something Gran had taught me to do.

Elementary astronomy and technology are the last things you would *choose* to do if you were alone in the Domestic Living Unit with Gran. Because those times are brilliant times. Listening to Gran talk about the olden days is like having a busy picture painted for you in front of your very eyes. It's the only thing in the whole of the wide universe that's better than imagining.

'Bye!'

I lay back on my bed and looked around. Welcome to my BedCube. Yawn. Bore. A curved white ceiling reflects a pool of gentle light all round. All the furniture is moulded in pastel laminates: a pale pink dressing-table, soft green bed and chairs, grey VDU, grey TeleSatScreen. Yawn. Bore.

'What are you complaining about?' That's what Dad always says: 'It's clean and it's spacious and it's warm and it's comfortable....'

And it's just like *their* BedCube.

And it's just like Gran's BedCube.

It's just like every other cube in our Domestic Living Unit and every other Domestic Living Unit on the European Space Colony (Taurus IV).

And probably just like every Domestic Living Unit on Aquarius and Pisces, too. Not that I've ever been there.

I heard the hiss of the Domestic Living Unit door closing as Mum and Dad left for the Wilkinses. I listened, then counted to five; listened again. All was quiet. I sat up, swung my legs round and leapt off the bed.

I pushed the bright green button by my BedCube door. It swished open. It always does. Yawn. Bore. Nothing ever breaks down on the European Space Colony (Taurus IV). I padded across the walkway and pushed the bright green button outside Gran's BedCube door. It swished open. Of course.

'Gran? Are you asleep?'

She usually has a nap in the evenings.

'Yes. Out for the count. Snore, snore.'

'Eh? Oh Gran....'

'Well, come on in if you're going to, you great wally.'

Gran's BedCube is well, exactly like my BedCube; except for our secret. Which is a box of ancient relics under the bed. On very special occasions and only when Mum and Dad are out we open the box up and look at and touch the relics. Ancient relics are strictly forbidden in Domestic Living Units on the European Space Colony (Taurus IV). Which makes Gran a criminal. And probably me, too.

'What's a great wally, Gran?'

'Eh? Oh, I don't know. It's an old-fashioned phrase. Something my mum often used to call my dad.'

'Yes, but what does it *mean*?'

'Well... I suppose... twit.'

'Eh?'

'Well, what does your mum call you when you've been a bit silly?

'A proper dilt.'

'There you are then. Great wally is just an old-fashioned phrase meaning a proper dilt. Now, what do you want for supper?'

Supper. Yawn. Bore.

I went to Gran's dressing-table and entered the code on her VDU – RO:JE:MA. I like my code RO:JE:MA. I often say it in my head as one word: Rojema. Sometimes in my imaginings, I call myself Rojema, rather than Rosemary. The screen flashed up:

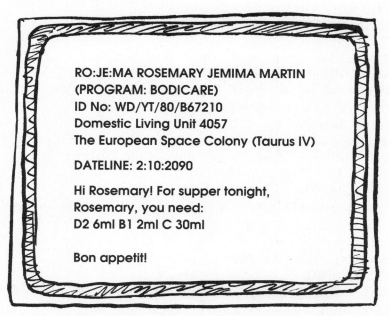

RO:JE:MA ROSEMARY JEMIMA MARTIN
(PROGRAM: BODICARE)
ID No: WD/YT/80/B67210
Domestic Living Unit 4057
The European Space Colony (Taurus IV)

DATELINE: 2:10:2090

Hi Rosemary! For supper tonight,
Rosemary, you need:
D2 6ml B1 2ml C 30ml

Bon appetit!

If that was what the Bodicare Program said I wanted for supper, that was what I'd got to have for supper. Three tablets popped out of the dispenser and I swallowed them all in one giant gulp.

'Gran, did the Elizabethans have tablets for supper?'

'Of course not.'

'What did they have then?'

Gran looked around and listened intently. She leaned over towards me.

'Promise you'll tell no one I told you.'

'Promise.'

'Cross your heart; hope to die?'

'Cross my heart; hope to die, Gran.'

That was another Elizabethan phrase Gran had taught me. She put her head close to mine; I could hear her breathing very quickly.

'Dead plants and animals.'

My stomach suddenly felt as if it was being pulled up towards my throat.

'Dead plants and animals?'

Gran nodded. Her face was as steady as a rock.

'And they had a special delicacy....'

If dead plants and animals were the Elizabethans' usual diet, I wasn't sure I wanted to hear about their special delicacies. But already Gran was whispering in my ear:

'Fishes' fingers.'

My stomach was creeping up the back of my tongue. This had to be one of Gran's famous wind-ups.

'Fishes didn't have fingers. I know; I've seen graphics of them on the history disk.'

'Huh, history disk; mystery disk,' muttered Gran, darkly. 'Of course the graphics you saw of fishes on the history disk didn't have any fingers and do you know why?'

I shook my head.

'The Elizabethans had eaten them all for their supper.'

'Urgh. But why did the Elizabethans eat fishes' fingers?'

Gran shrugged. 'The taste I suppose.'

'Taste?'

'Yes... taste. Flavour. A sense they used to have.'

'What was it like?'

'Like? Oh... I can't describe it. Any more than you can describe shades and colours. I mean, can you describe "pink" to me?'

'Pink? Well, it's sort of... light red.'

'Sort of light red! What's that meant to tell me? I suppose if I asked you to describe "red", you'd say it was sort of dark pink?'

'Er....'

I took Gran's point.

'There you are then. No one can describe colour or taste. Smell – that was another one.'

'Smell?'

'You used your nose for smelling.'

It sounded horrid.

'I remember your great-grandfather lighting a fire. Made from wood. In the open air. That was some smell. Wood smoke.'

Gran's eyes had glazed over. She seemed to be looking somewhere way out beyond the dreamy-white ceiling of the BedCube.

'I miss those tastes and smells,' she said, quietly.

Roy Apps

MAKING GOOD

What we need is a new bus

Not so long ago an old red bus ran down to the station and back again. It was a rumbling-grumbling bus. It was a rusty-dusty bus. It was a jumping-bumping bus. And because it was all of these things some people walked to the station rather than ride in the old bus. It shook them about too much.

'The trouble with this old bus,' the driver said, 'is that it's worn out. It needs a new engine to drive it. It needs new tyres to run on. It needs new seats, new windows, new paint, new everything. In fact what we need is a *new* bus!'

Now the bus wasn't surprised to hear this. It did feel worn out. It was worn out. Climbing the hills made its engine work so hard it went slower and slower and slower. Changing gears all the time made it feel exhausted. All it wanted to do was sleep in the sun for ever.

'*Ur, ur, ur!*' it grumbled. It didn't want to go another wheel turn.

Inside the bus the conductor was calling out. 'Fares, pliz! Fares! Fares, pliz!' He sold pink tickets from his book to the passengers, and their money dropped into his big black bag with a tinkling plink, plink, plink.

And inside the bus the driver was in his seat in front of the big steering wheel. He pushed the gear lever into place. He pulled off the brake and before it knew what was happening the old red bus was rolling down the road again.

'*Urr-uuuuur-urrrr-urrrrr!*' It grumbled. It mumbled. It groaned. '*Grrrr!* It was as if it couldn't go another wheel turn. And to its surprise the old red bus didn't.

Sssssss!

The front tyre was shrinking smaller and smaller. *Sssssssss!* What was happening to the plump round sides? *Sssssssss!* Air hissed out. The tyre was as flat as a piece of paper.

The driver stopped the bus. Out he jumped. Out jumped the bus conductor. People poked their heads from their windows.

'The front tyre is as flat as a pancake,' the driver told them. 'We can't fix it here. You'd better walk to the station.'

'We'd better get the mechanic from the garage,' said the conductor. 'We could be here for hours,' he told the people. 'Yes, you'd be better off walking to the station.'

Now the people grumbled and mumbled and groaned and moaned and walked to the station. 'What we need is a new bus,' they muttered and some of them stopped to look at the flat tyre that had run over a big nail. It had stabbed a hole in the tyre's tube. *Sssssss!* Out hissed the air until the tyre, no longer fat and round, looked saggy-baggy, as flat as flat. A sad limp tyre.

When, at last, the mechanic came roaring up in his truck he tapped the old red bus with a spanner and said, 'This old crate needs more than a new tyre.'

'I know, I know,' agreed the bus driver. 'What we need is a new bus. When can you sell us one?'

'Not today.' The mechanic shook his head. He banged and tapped and looked at the insides of the bus and said nothing for a long time, then he said, 'In a couple of weeks we could make this old bus almost as good as new, up at the garage.'

Now that was a good idea. A wonderful idea, especially for the old bus. It helped as much as it could when the tow-truck came. There was a crane on the back of the tow-truck and it lifted the front wheels of the bus away, away off the ground. With just its two back wheels the old red bus ran along behind the tow-truck to the garage.

And when some people saw the old red bus being towed away they decided that it must be going to the scrap-heap. Where else could it go? 'Looks as if we'll get a new bus after all,' they told each other.

At the garage, mechanics took out the worn parts of the engine and put in new ones. They oiled and greased. They fitted new tyres and new seats. They repainted and repainted the old bus a sparkling red, a shiny red, a geranium red. It didn't look like an old bus. It didn't feel like an old bus. It felt like running a thousand miles or two – up hills, down hills and along lumpy, bumpy roads.

When the time came for the old red bus to drive along the road to the station everyone wanted a ride. They crowded in. Some people sat and some people had to stand. The bus was loaded but up the hill it went without a grumble or rumble, just a little *gr-grr-grrr* which was like a happy humming song. 'This isn't bad for our old red bus!' said the conductor with a grin.

'Not our old rumbling, grumbling bus!' shrieked someone. 'This can't be our old, dusty, rusty bus! Don't tell me that this is the bumpy, jumpy, worn-out old bus!'

It was, and we know that it was, don't we?

Jean Chapman

That's nothing but junk, Josie

I always find perfectly good things in the bin. My family always says that whatever's in the bin is junk, but it never looks like junk to me. So I always ask, 'Are you sure it's junk?' They're always sure.

Well, the other day I found such perfectly good things, I thought everyone had made a mistake.

Mum threw out: a cardboard tube from the kitchen roll; a nice soft handbag with only a broken zip and a torn handle; and a place mat shaped like a daisy.

I said, 'Mum! Look what you threw away!'

Mum looked. 'That's nothing but junk, Josie.'

'Are you sure?'

'If that isn't junk,' Mum said, 'then I don't know what junk is.'

I used the cardboard tube for a telescope. I put all my seashells in the handbag. Then I played dressing-up and wore the pretty place mat as my hat.

I don't think Mum really knows what junk is.

Dad threw out: two jokers from some polka-dot cards; four pieces of green string; and a nightlight from when I was little. It had three cracks in it, but it might still work.

I said, 'Dad! Look what you threw away!'

Dad looked. 'That's nothing but junk, Josie.'

'Are you sure?'

'If that isn't junk,' Dad said, 'then I don't know what junk is.'

I put the jokers in my scrapbook. They looked pretty. I tied the strings together and made a belt. Then I turned on the nightlight switch. It worked!

I don't think Dad really knows what junk is.

My big brother Martin threw out: a big bow that I put on his birthday present; sunglasses with only one side missing; and a bright red T-shirt he said was too raggedy for anyone to wear.

I said, 'Martin! Look what you threw away!'

Martin looked. 'That's nothing but junk, Josie.'

'Are you sure?'

'If that isn't junk,' Martin said, 'then I don't know what junk is.'

My place-mat hat looked even better after I pasted the bow on it. I looked through my telescope with my sunglasses on. I could spy even better. Then I put on the T-shirt. I would not call it raggedy!

I don't think Martin really knows what junk is.

The very next day Mum and Dad said they were going to paint the kitchen, the hall and Martin's room. (Last time they painted my room, the living room and the bathroom.)

They all started cleaning. Mum cleaned the shelves. Dad cleaned out cabinets. Martin finally cleaned his wardrobe.

They began filling up boxes, bags, a wheelbarrow, Martin's old wagon and my old dolls's pram with all sorts of stuff.

'What are you going to do with all that?' I asked.

'Don't worry,' Mum said. But I was worried. They could be throwing out lots of perfectly good things.

'Don't worry,' Dad said. But even I couldn't pull that much stuff out of the bin.

'We're just throwing out some things,' Martin said.

'Oh, no!' I said. And I tried not to bite my nails.

Then, to my relief Mum brought the bags to my room.

'Have fun,' she said.

And Dad brought the boxes. 'It's all yours, Josie,' he said.

And Martin came with the wheelbarrow, the wagon, and the pram. 'I didn't say where we're throwing them,' he said.

At first I was very happy. But it didn't last.

What could I do with a bell that wouldn't ring? Or six loose pages with funny spelling on them? And who wanted a silly white chip pasted to an old cardboard? Or a brush with scrunched-up bristles? And who cared about a key that didn't fit anything? Or a smashed acorn?

It took me a long time to look at everything. But there wasn't even one perfectly good thing.

There has to be something else perfectly good somewhere, I thought. So I cleaned my wardrobe (even though I keep my things very neat). All I found was a harmonica with four broken notes, mittens that didn't fit, and a silly game Aunt Louise once gave me.

I put my stuff with everyone else's.

'Please come get your things!' I called. 'And take mine, too. It's all nothing but junk!'

First Mum came. 'This isn't junk,' she said. 'These pages are the missing part of my French cookbook. And here's the key to my old diary! Oh, and these mittens will fit your little cousin, Adrienne.'

Then Dad came. 'This isn't junk,' he said. 'Here's the only good broom around. And this is Martin's first tooth.' (That was the chip on the cardboard.) 'Ah, I haven't played a harmonica in years!' He went out tootling.

Then Martin came. 'This isn't junk,' he said. 'Here's the acorn from my last scout camp. And this is the bell from my old tricycle. And I *told* Aunt Louise you were too young for this game!'

'BUT IF THAT ISN'T JUNK,' I said to everyone, 'THEN I DON'T KNOW WHAT JUNK IS!'

But no one heard me.

Mum was reading her diary.

Dad was tootling away on his harmonica.

Martin was spinning the game spinner.

'Can I play?' I asked him.

'Okay,' he said. 'But don't forget. It's my game now. So don't use it without asking.'

I don't think *anyone* really knows what junk is.

Phyllis Rose Eisenberg

Dustbin Charlie

The rain plonked down in bucketfuls and nothing happened for ages. Only three people walked down Union Street: Curly Harry, the tramp who slept in the park, old Mrs Batts, who lived at Number 23, and Frank, the paper-boy.

Curly Harry had a plastic carrier-bag on his head to keep the rain off. Mrs Batts had a red umbrella. Frank didn't have anything at all and his wet hair hung down like black string.

Charlie decided to go and help Grandma make cakes. He was just going through the door when he heard a noise in the street. A huge red truck had stopped outside Number 10 and some men were getting out of it.

'It's the builders,' he said to himself and he climbed on to the chair again to see what happened.

First they propped the front door open with a brick. Then the boss stood in the back of the truck and handed things down — hammers and shovels and bags of cement. When everything had been unloaded, the truck moved off. Then they all went inside and had cups of tea. Charlie could see them through the dirty windows.

The rain still sloshed down. 'No outside work today,' said the boss, looking up at the sky from the doorway of Number 10. 'We can't do much anyway, not till the skip comes,' and he shut the rickety old door.

Charlie went down the garden to Grandad's shed. He was making toast on Mrs Next Door's toaster. 'Have a piece,' he said, 'I've fixed it.'

'What's a skip?' asked Charlie, munching away.

'It's a great big box, for putting rubbish in. Want some more?'

'Yes, please. Is a skip bigger than a dustbin?'

'*Much* bigger.'

'Well, they're getting one for Number 10.'

'Told you they'd be throwing stuff out, didn't I?' said Grandad. Then, 'Oh, *heck*!' Slice of bread number two had stuck in the toaster and the shed was full of black smoke.

'I'll have to start again with this,' he said, scratching his shiny bald head.

Charlie slipped a bit of burnt toast into his pocket (it was good for drawing pictures with), then he went back to see what the builders were doing.

The big red truck had come back with the skip. It was lowering it on to the road outside Number 10 with a great clanking noise. All the men stood round watching. So did Curly Harry. The rain dripped off his carrier-bag hat and sploshed into the puddles. 'Easy does it!' shouted the boss, and the skip hit the pavement with a loud boomy sound.

Charlie went up close to get a better look. It was a huge iron box, thin at the bottom and fat at the top, and it was painted banana yellow. Inside there was room for ten dustbins and twenty Charlies. That skip was nearly as big as Grandma's kitchen.

It sat there all day. The builders kept popping out of Number 10 to throw things into it – old floor-boards and rusty pipes, half a cooker and a broken-down TV. But Charlie could only watch till dinner. In the afternoon they all wrapped up warm and went to visit Aunty Alice across the park.

When they got back, the builders had gone home, but the shiny yellow skip was still outside Number 10. It was piled high with rubbish now, but Grandad said the red truck would be back first thing tomorrow to empty it. Charlie got worried. He wanted to have a good look at all that stuff before it disappeared.

Grandma didn't like him grubbing about in the dirt, so he sneaked out while she was running his bath. He couldn't see over the top, so he stuck his hands in the air and pulled himself up. Then he looked in.

The skip wasn't just full of builders' rubbish, there were lots of other things too. People must have come along Union Street and slipped them in while the men weren't looking. They all looked like things that were no use any more, things that should go to the dump. It was quicker using the skip though.

Under the Number 10 rubbish Charlie saw a big blue blanket with holes in. Then he saw a baby's pram with crumpled wheels. Then he saw a cracked sink with no taps.

He was just about to climb down when he saw IT. So he swung himself up again.

IT was lying on top of the blue blanket with its feet under some planks. It was all rusty and dented and its silver paint had been scratched right off. But it still had two arms and two legs and the wonderful smile on its face that Charlie remembered so well. It was the Walking Tin Man from the TV advert, the one that cost a year's pocket-money.

'Sorry, Charlie,' Dad had said when he had wanted it for his birthday. 'Toys like that cost big money, and we need some new cows.' Instead, he'd had an aeroplane book and some new jeans. They weren't nearly as good as the Walking Tin Man.

Charlie leaned right down into the skip and pulled till the Tin Man sat upright with a clonking sound. The little door in its back was open and the works were sticking out. All the wires and springs inside were bust. You'd have to be a genious to mend it now. The poor old Tin Man would never walk again.

He still wanted it, though. It was nearly as big as he was. It'd look great in his bedroom. He tugged and tugged, trying to get it out from under the planks. Then a voice across the street shouted, 'Charlie? *Charlie*! What are you doing, grubbing about in that dirty old skip? I've been calling you for ten minutes, and your bath's going cold!' It was Grandma, with a fluffy striped towel over her arm. She sounded a bit mad.

Charlie went inside and followed her up the stairs. He was trying to tell her about the Tin Man, but she was rather deaf. 'A *tin can*?' she said. 'What on earth do you want with an old *tin can*? There are plenty of those in your Grandad's shed. Now come on, this water's getting cold.'

But he thought about the poor Tin Man all through his bath and afterwards, when Grandad read him a story. Before going to sleep, he lifted the curtains and peeped out. The big yellow skip gleamed gently in the light from the street lamp, and there was Curly Harry, poking about inside it with a stick. He was still wearing his plastic-bag hat.

Old Mrs Batts came along with her dog, Jim. She stopped by the skip too and peered over the side. Then Frank came up on his bicycle. He was on his evening round and the front basket was full of papers. He stood up on his pedals and looked at all the rubbish, then he pulled at something, but it wouldn't come out. Everyone was interested in that skip.

'It's got a walking man in it,' Charlie said sleepily as Grandad tucked him in. But Grandma switched the light off. 'A talking *pan*? You need a good night's sleep,' she said.

'Sweet dreams, Charlie,' whispered Grandad.

And they were sweet. They were about him and the Tin Man, walking round the farmyard hand in hand.

Ann Pilling

Charley and the machines

Charley was a boy who spent a lot of time alone.
His father was very very busy.
His mother was very very busy.
His big brother was extraordinarily busy,
and the baby was asleep.
So Charley had to look after the others.

There were the Moon Brothers out by the back door:
fat, square, moon-faced and unpredictable,
and always hungry,
You had to watch them or they'd have the
clothes off your back.
Charley did his best to keep them fed.
He got mud on his trousers and egg on his shirt,
spilt tomato ketchup on his socks
and got wet every time it rained.
But they never seemed satisfied.
'Give me more, more' mumbled one,
mouth full of bubbles.
'Dry 'em, dry 'em,' grumbled the other,
puffing steam at the cat.

The monster under the stairs was just as hungry.
From time to time it would roar out,
trailing a snaking tail behind
and gobbling up everything in front.
Charley did his best with a litter of crumbs
and rubbish all over the floor.
But when he wasn't looking
it would sneak up and swallow
titbits of LEGO too, and papers
with important messages on them.
When he went to ask for them back
he found it sleeping off the feast
under the stairs in the dark.
It didn't care.

In the kitchen was Big Cool.
Big Cool was wise. Big Cool was cool.
He didn't move. He didn't roar.
He just chuckled quietly in the corner from time to time.
That was the place for a bit of peace.
Charley and Big Cool had an understanding.
Charley kept him company and
when no one was looking
Big Cool would unbutton his coat
and whip out a drink, a bit of cheese
or sometimes even an ice-cream.

If the Gang saw them there was trouble.
Kettle Suzie in a fury puffed and rattled with scalding steam.
Mick the Mad Mixer rocked and whined:
'Gimme some. I'll smash it! I'll grind it!'
And as Charley turned round, the toaster,
Pop the Toaster, hurled
a left-over piece of burnt toast across the room.
Their wires got tangled.
Their handles got sticky.
Their fuses blew.
And Charley would sort them out.
But he never knew when another one would start up:
the driller in the basement
the sewing machine in the hall.

After that, there was only one place to go.
Across the hall, and shut the door, to see the Magician Queen.
She told him stories, and took him to the other side of the world,
drew pictures, played music. She could make him laugh and
make him sigh.
And quite often she sang him to sleep.

Kathy Henderson

James the Jumble

Once upon a time there was an untidy bedroom, a very untidy bedroom. It belonged to a boy called James. James made such a mess, whatever he did, that his mum called him James the Jumble.

'James, James the Jumble,' she would call, 'come and look at this room. It's *awful*!'

There were sweet-papers on the floor, crumpled clothes in every corner, scribbled papers sticking out of the drawers, crisps in the bed, toys spread all over the carpet, and comics falling off the window-sill. When his mum tried to make the bed she tripped up on rolling marbles and pens, while his dad kept on vacuuming up the LEGO. The untidy room made both his parents cross.

'Tidy up *NOW*, James the Jumble, or you'll have *NO TEA!*'

So James would open the wardrobe and drawers and stuff the mess in there instead. The room then *looked* better, but if you opened a cupboard door everything tumbled out on to the floor again.

Now, the untidy bedroom had had enough. Its sides ached with the weight of all the toys shoved on its shelves; its walls itched where James had scribbled on them; its cupboard doors creaked painfully, fit to burst with all the junk trying to force its way out; its floor was choked with dust because there was no space to vacuum.

One afternoon James the Jumble decided he wanted an adventure playground upstairs. He hung up fraying string ladders and slung ropes across between the door handles. When his mum popped out to the shop for bread, James dragged in a dirty plank from the garden and balanced it between the bed and the chest of drawers.

At last, the untidy room could stand it no more. It decided to run away.

James was just practising his Tarzan jungle call when he felt the room move. He was swinging halfway up a rope ladder at the time so he just thought, 'Cor, I went all dizzy'. Then a moment later the room gave a powerful shudder and

James crashed to the floor. This time he was really frightened. The room was bumping and banging all over the place, making enormous shivers as it tore itself away from the rest of the house. Then, with a sudden, crashing jerk, the room pulled free, shook itself, and set off along the drive.

All the toys, books, and clutter poured off the shelves and landed on James the Jumble. Everything was bouncing all around him and the dirty plank had tumbled across the fallen wardrobe so James was trapped behind. Marbles, pens and pingpong balls rolled off the open end of the room as it progressed down the road.

The untidy bedroom caused quite a stir when it turned the corner and reached the shops. No one had ever seen a room walking down the road before.

Gill Davies

The lonely skyscraper

There was once a very tall skyscraper who stood by himself in the middle of many roads. The roads went over and under each other and round and round. Sometimes they disappeared into the ground and came up again a long way off. All the skyscraper could see was roads, stretching into the distance. During the day, cars and buses whizzed by and lorries thundered past in all directions.

The skyscraper was full of people who worked in him. They banged his doors and talked and laughed. They zoomed up and down in his lifts and swished in and out of his automatic doors.

Some of the people scrubbed and polished him until he gleamed more than ever before. But he was sad, because he was nobody's home. At night, the skyscraper stood alone, feeling big and echoey inside. It got cold and dark and silent and he was very, very lonely.

One clear day in early spring, the skyscraper was looking at his view when, from his very top windows, he saw something green beyond the endless grey of the winding roads.

'I wonder what that is,' he thought to himself. He had never seen the countryside, so he didn't know what it looked like. But every day after that, he gazed into the distance at the thin line of green. He could see houses far away, small and neat enough to fit under the trees. It all looked so peaceful.

'If only I could live there,' sighed the skyscraper.

That night he made up his mind to go.

First he rocked to one side. All the pencils and typewriters flew across the room and crashed against the walls.

'OUCH!' he said.

Then he rocked to the other side. All the typewriters and pencils flew back across to the opposite walls.

'OUCH!' he said again.

Next, he took his first step. CRUNCH! The noise of the skyscraper walking was louder than the noise of all the cars and lorries put together.

By sunrise, he had walked across

all the grey roads and had just reached the beginning of the countryside that he was longing to see. For the first time in his life, the skyscraper heard birds singing. He smelled the fresh, spring flowers as they opened towards the sun. He passed trees with more green leaves on them than he could count. The muddy country path felt cool and comfortable after walking on the hard city streets.

As the sun rose, so did the skyscraper's spirits. BOOM! CRASH! TINKLE! he went, as he walked along. The sun's beams glinted and flashed on his many windows. He had changed from grey to pink and orange, with gleams of green where grass and trees shone in his glass. If he'd known how to whistle he certainly would have done, from sheer happiness.

Soon he came to a field with a stream running round it and some sleepy black and white cows munching on the thick grass.

'What a lovely place to live!' thought the skyscraper, and he walked right through the fence into the middle of the field.

'Help!' cried the cows. 'A monster!' and they all ran away.

A few minutes later an angry farmer with a red face came running down the road, waving a large stick. 'Get off my land!' he shouted, and he beat his stick against the skyscraper's gleaming front doors. Of course, the skyscraper hardly noticed the stick, although it was heavy. But he didn't like feeling unwanted, so he moved away slowly.

'Where can I go?' he wondered. 'I'm too big to live here.' He felt huge and ugly in the pretty green field.

Suddenly a voice said, 'Don't tread on me!'

The skyscraper bent down his top floors and gazed at the ground. He saw a tiny brown bird.

'I'll show you a place to live,' said the bird. 'It's the most beautiful place in the world. Let me come in and I'll take you there.' SWOOSH! The skyscraper opened his shiny doors and the little bird hopped in.

As spring turned into summer, they travelled on. When it rained, the skyscraper went BOOM! SPLASH! TINKLE! SPLOSH! through all the muddy puddles.

At last they came to a great forest.

'Here we are!' cried the little bird.

'How shall I get through all those trees?' asked the skyscraper. But the trees bent aside to let him pass and he went BOOM! TINKLE! CRUNCH! SWISH! over the grassy floor.

They came to a space in the middle of the forest.

'This will do,' said the little bird, so the skyscraper sat down.

KERUMP! BOOM! BUMP!

Then he arranged himself comfortably on the moss and looked round in all directions to see what was near him.

From his front windows, he saw rolling hills and fields with sheep and cattle grazing quietly in the afternoon sun.

From one side, he saw the sea, with a steamer trailing smoke along the horizon, and fishing boats and seagulls.

From the other side, he saw a village with leafy lanes winding between small cottages and gardens full of pretty flowers.

Far behind him, he saw the grey line of the distant city.

'So much to see and hear and smell,' thought the skyscraper.

When summer was over, birds arrived to nest in his trays. Squirrels stored nuts in his paper cups. Mice lived in drawers and cabinets. Pencils were nibbled up for nests. Badgers slept on sofas, and moles tunnelled under the thick carpets. At bedtime, rabbits wrapped their babies in typewriter ribbons. Small insects were bathed in the inkwells. Baby voles cut their teeth on files marked 'IMPORTANT' and little mice were tucked into all sorts of beds.

The skyscraper soon got used to all the furry tickles and bumps, but one winter day there seemed to be more activity than usual.

'What is happening now?' he asked the little brown bird.

'We're getting ready for a party,' she replied. 'A skyscraper-warming party!'

'But I'm warm enough already,' said the skyscraper, who did not feel the cold with all the animals inside him. But the bird had already flown off to find her friends.

In the main dining room, all the animals were busy laying out a tempting feast on the shiny table tops. Before long, the skyscraper began to glow in the dazzling light of the setting sun. It was time for the party to begin.

Soon, sounds of merry-making rang through the snowy forest and the skyscraper was amazed to find himself growing warmer and warmer. It was a special sort of warmth, which spread from his top floors right down to his basement. Even his draughty halls felt snug, and his windy staircase cosy.

He remembered when he had stood by himself at night feeling cold, sad and lonely. Suddenly he laughed out loud! Now he knew what a 'skyscraper-warming' party really meant.

At last he was somebody's HOME.

Jenny Hawkesworth

Surrounded by bridges

It all began with a nursery rhyme. Imagine!

There we were, the whole class, thinking our new teacher Mr McKenzie had dimmed his lights and gone barmy. It was the first day, the first lesson and virtually the first minute of a new term and Mr McKenzie, having just finished the register, started singing a nursery rhyme:

'London Bridge is falling down,
Falling down, falling down,
London Bridge is falling down
My fair lady!'

As he got to the 'My fair lady' part I could feel myself whispering the ending I knew, 'My scary baby'. But I thought I would keep that for playtime!

'Did the bridge actually fall down?' I asked him as he finished the rhyme.

'Yes Michael, it did fall down and fairly regularly,' he replied.

'What, just like Kevin's PE shorts?' I laughed and the rest of the class all giggled. Kevin didn't mind; he was used to it by now. He's one of my mates and he has trouble with elastic. He seems to spend every PE lesson with one hand keeping his shorts up and the other hand trying to stop himself falling over.

'Well, perhaps not quite as often, but it certainly had its problems. You see London Bridge has been swept away by a storm, burned down, destroyed by a flood and its foundations worn away by the pressure of the water flowing through the narrow piers it used to have.'

'So I take it, Mr McKenzie, from your reference to bridges, that we are about to undertake some work on the subject,' said Imran. He's my other mate and you could say a bit quick on the trigger when it comes to school work. In fact, he's so clever, sometimes I think he invented brains. He certainly knows the difference between Pancake Tuesday and half-past breakfast time which is more than can be said for some of my class!

'Yes, well, as our topic for this term is "Structures", I thought it would get us off to an interesting start if we had a "Bridge Week" and that means....'

Well, what it meant was, for that week, we had plenty of weighing, problem solving, drawing, reading, writing and stories on, yes you guessed it, bridges! We even had a PE lesson on bridges where we all had to make bridges with our bodies. At one stage I had Kevin for a partner and our bridge kept collapsing because Kevin kept pulling his hand away to keep those PE shorts up!

As the week went on we learned that there are bridges all around us and not always where we would expect to find them. For example, we are surrounded by simple structures that act like bridges. Beds, washing lines, shelves and tables all of which in their own way support a weight. Why even our noses have bridges in them. Some bigger than others!

Mr McKenzie told us that today bridges are used to carry railways, roads and people where they wish to go, but the first bridges were used by Stone Age hunters in their search for food. A fallen tree or carefully placed log would allow the hunters to pursue their prey across deep streams.

As the week went on, I found it interesting to discover all the different types of bridge designs there are. Simple arch bridges that can often be seen across small rivers and streams were built by the Romans. They discovered that an arch made a very strong shape and the fact these bridges have lasted so long proves them right. Other types of bridges which use arches in their structure are *viaducts*. These bridges are used to carry roads and railways over difficult land or across river valleys. They usually have several layers of arches stacked on top of each other with the trains or cars running over the top row.

On Wednesday when we were in the library Kevin and I found a picture of a rope bridge. It was drawn in a jungle and this set Kevin off. Suddenly he was Tarzan swinging on a vine across a clearing and off he went swinging across the library pretending he was Tarzan, 'UURRGGHH UURRGGHH!' Unfortunately he swung straight into the headteacher. Now when our headteacher catches you messing about she doesn't say anything. No, she just lets her, cold grey eyes parachute down on top of you and then follows them up with the rest of her head. She gets so close that you think she's going to taste you. It really unnerves everyone and as far as I'm concerned makes my hair curl which takes some doing as it's as straight as a pencil. But it usually has the required result and on the whole everyone in our school behaves themselves quite well.

Anyway the rope bridge led on to Imran, Kevin and myself having great fun trying to build a suspension bridge. We discovered that it can span greater distances than any other type of bridge and one that is similar to a rope bridge in basic design, but instead of rope uses iron. You see, the roadway hangs down on great iron chains from two towers rather than being supported on piers. Anyway, our group got two chairs, a metre stick and a ball of string. We placed the chairs back to back and just over a metre apart and connected them with two pieces of string like two tight ropes. From these tight ropes we looped eight other pieces of string so we ended up with a sort of cradle to lie the metre stick along. Then Imran began carefully piling books on to the metre stick to see what weight the bridge would hold. When he got to eight the chairs toppled in towards the books and our string bridge collapsed. Unfortunately, the books landed 'Bang – OW!' right on Kevin's toe. So now he's got his toe to hold on to as well as his PE shorts.

Our group, with Imran in charge, also had to carry out some work with pieces of card and marbles. This was to find out which shapes made the strongest structures for bridges. We folded the card in all sorts of different ways. It was surprising how different shapes were so much stronger than others and held a lot more marbles.

Anyway, on Friday morning after assembly, Mr McKenzie announced that there was to be a bridge building competition. We had the morning to work on a bridge that would cross a space of 30cm and at the same time support a weight of one kilogram. We were allowed a limited amount of newspaper, card, straws and junk material. Mr McKenzie also told us to consider the work we had covered during the week and think which type of bridge and design of structure would be strongest for the task. He then briefly told us about an infamous bridge disaster that happened in Scotland over a hundred years ago. It was in the year 1879 and a train travelling from Edinburgh to Dundee had to cross over the River Tay. A new bridge had only been opened eighteen months previously by Queen Victoria. The train set out across the bridge at the height of a storm and it never reached the other side. The storm had blown the bridge down and the train with it. At least seventy-five people lost their lives on that terrible night. Mr McKenzie told us that the bridge designer had been blamed because he had not made the bridge strong enough to withstand the powerful Tay Valley winds. He also had not supervised the building of the bridge where the workmanship was poor and the iron they used of inferior quality. All the class groups seemed to take note and set off to design as strong a bridge as possible!

Well, we didn't win the competition but our bridge fared pretty well and came third. It held up 900 grams and then decided enough was enough and collapsed. Imran reckoned if we could have had another go we definitely would have solved the problem. But I said the chap who designed the first Tay Bridge probably thought that as well. Anyway, we didn't disgrace ourselves, not like the group on the next table. They were all secretive and told us to keep our nostrils out of their 'fantastic' design. But we had the last laugh because it fell down before a single weight was put on it. Kevin reckoned a spider walked across it!

Guess what? A girl's group won the competition! Guess what? Their group leader's name was Bridget! Guess what? It was Kevin's birthday last week! Yes, you've guessed. He got a new pair of PE shorts!

Ian Souter

Parker-Hamilton

Mr and Mrs Brown and Jacqueline thought their new robot was terrific. Only Grandma wasn't very impressed. 'Ridiculous-looking thing, if you ask me,' she said, with her nose in the air.

'It's going to be worth every penny,' Mrs Brown contradicted. She pressed the robot's starter button and said, giggling a little, 'We'd like afternoon tea, please.' The robot glided on soundless wheels to the kitchen.

'It's creepy, that's what,' said Grandma. 'It'd better not break any of my rose pattern china, either.'

'That robot has a hundred per cent efficiency guarantee,' said Mr Brown. The new robot served an excellent cup of tea and also baked some beautifully light scones.

'We ought to give it a name,' said Jacqueline, reading the manual. 'You have to feed in a selection of names, and it chooses the one it likes best.' The

Browns thought of various names and wrote them down on pieces of paper and placed them in the robot's input slot. But all the names were firmly rejected.

'Well, it's one of the more expensive models,' said Mrs Brown. 'I suppose it's inclined to be a bit fussy.'

'It's just plain stuck-up,' said Grandma. Mrs Brown wrote down stuck-up names such as Montague and Forsythe, and when she wrote down Parker-Hamilton with a hyphen, the robot flashed a green light.

The Browns had a wonderful time watching Parker-Hamilton do jobs. Mr Brown's business account books were perfectly balanced with no effort on his part. Mrs Brown had the front door repainted and a manicure. Jacqueline's room looked tidy for the first time in years. Parker-Hamilton noiselessly removed the shoes and dumped jeans from under her bed, sorted out her records and repaired all the torn posters on her walls.

Grandma was the only one who didn't hang round admiring the new robot. 'I never did like any machine except television,' she said stubbornly.

'Parker-Hamilton could finish that bedspread you're crocheting,' Jacqueline suggested. She pushed the crochet pattern into the slot, and Parker-Hamilton whirred softly and slid out a perfect square of crochet in six seconds. The square of crochet was even sealed into a small hygienic plastic bag.

Grandma didn't look very grateful. She snatched back her crochet pattern and pushed the wool bag behind the couch. 'I'm not staying in the house with that interfering know-it-all,' she said crossly. 'I'll go to a hotel.' The robot helpfully packed her suitcase and dialled a taxi.

That night it cooked and served a wholesome, well-balanced, three-course meal. It passed the salt and pepper and even played some very nice violin dinner music. At the end of the meal it brought warm water and towels and washed everyone's hands. 'Oh, how cute!' said Mrs Brown.

Parker-Hamilton switched on the television in the living room and then went and did the washing up. At ten it went around the house and turned down everyone's bed. It took out the rubbish and locked the front door. Then it hovered in the hallway, humming quietly to itself, with its metal arms folded. Its panel of little lights flickered down to a soft glow.

'That's sweet,' said Jacqueline. 'It's put itself to sleep for the night.'

Mrs Brown had plenty of spare time from then on. She phoned Grandma at the hotel and announced triumphantly that she was thinking of taking up opera singing lessons now, because she had so much leisure. But Grandma only snorted and hung up in her ear.

The Brown household routine became dazzlingly efficient. Jacqueline had a pair of clean socks for school every morning without fail. And if she left a wad of used bubble gum on her desk or the bathroom basin, the robot removed it immediately. Jacqueline began to think that it followed her around on purpose because of the bubble gum, and it made her feel self-conscious.

'Everything certainly is well run around here,' Mrs Brown said, but she began to sound a little uncertain. Actually, the robot was becoming fiercely possessive about the housework. It hated to see newspapers left lying around, and it hovered by Mr Brown when he smoked his pipe, with an ashtray at the ready. 'Parker-Hamilton is getting a bit bossy,' said Mrs Brown. 'Do you know it washed the kitchen floor eighteen times today and then it locked the door and wouldn't let me in there to get a glass of water! Can't you adjust its mechanism, Roger, and tone it down a little?'

Mr Brown studied the manual. 'It certainly does need adjusting,' said Jacqueline. 'I'm not allowed to sit on my bed once it's made. Parker-Hamilton makes this scary buzzing noise.'

'I'm afraid this particular model can't be toned down,' said Mr Brown. 'It's designed to work at peak efficiency.'

'How clever,' said Mrs Brown, but she sounded a little annoyed. The house was so clean that the curtains hung like sheets of glass and every carpet fibre could be counted. All the books were arranged in perfect grading of size and each one was sealed in a hygienic plastic bag. Everything was so bright and shimmering that the Browns had to wear sunglasses.

Parker-Hamilton didn't like them strolling around the shiny house. It pushed them firmly into the kitchen and showed them a sheet of computer paper with printed instructions. It was a schedule of the times they were permitted to enter the living room.

'This is ridiculous,' said Mr Brown. 'We're only allowed in the living room to watch TV for one hour each day, and even then we have to wear plastic bags over our shoes. And it says we have to shampoo our hair out at the garden tap because it won't have the bathroom basin used.'

They sat down to an uneasy meal. Parker-Hamilton was beginning to be very high-handed about table manners. It rapped Jacqueline over the knuckles for spilling soup on the tablecloth and took away her dessert. Jacqueline burst into tears. 'I don't like it any more,' she cried. 'It's nothing but a big bully!'

Mr Brown worriedly studied the manual again. 'There's hundreds of pounds worth of electronic engineering behind that panel, and it's all been designed to produce a perfect household robot,' he said. 'There's no dial I can alter.'

Grandma came in with her suitcase. 'I only came home because I didn't like the marmalade at the hotel,' she said. 'I see you still have that contraption.'

The robot quickly whisked Grandma's suitcase away and unpacked it. Then it cleared away the meal dishes, and put the chairs in perfect alignment. Then it took all the Browns into the bathroom and they had their teeth cleaned for four minutes each. Parker-Hamilton put plastic bags over their shoes, and they were allowed to go into the living room.

They all looked terribly self-conscious and didn't meet Grandma's eyes. 'Why are we watching this boring programme about diesel engines?' Grandma asked.

'Parker-Hamilton chooses each night,' said Mrs Brown miserably. 'It likes films about engines and motors. It gets annoyed if we change over channels.'

'I always watch the race reviews on a Sunday evening,' said Grandma. 'And where's my crochet?'

'Parker-Hamilton finished it off,' said Jacqueline, taking a bundle from the cupboard. It was Grandma's bedspread, completely finished, down to the last six hundred and fortieth tiny perfect square. It was sealed into a plastic bag. 'Parker-Hamilton doesn't like unfinished work left lying about,' said Jacqueline.

Grandma stared at her rug indignantly. 'Years and years of work I'd done on that rug!' she yelled. 'And it was good for another fifteen years yet! Now that nosey-parker's gone and ruined all the pleasure!'

'We certainly didn't bargain for it taking over the house like this,' said Mr Brown.

'Send it back to the factory,' snapped Grandma.

'They don't accept models back,' said Mr Brown sheepishly. 'I've already telephoned.'

Parker-Hamilton's lights blinked and he made a buzzing hornet sound. 'It means we have to be quiet while this documentary's on,' said Mrs Brown. But Grandma turned the television to her race programme. Parker-Hamilton buzzed rapidly and more loudly.

'Don't you dare speak to me like that!' Grandma ordered. The high-pitched buzzing suddenly stopped. All the angry flashing little lights snapped off, and the robot stood quietly in the middle of the room with its metal arms folded. 'That's better,' said Grandma. She sat down and began to unravel the crochet rug. Mrs Brown and Mr Brown and Jacqueline all stared at her.

'What happened?' they demanded. 'How did you do that?'

Grandma held up the end of an electric flex. 'I just switched it off at the wall and pulled out the plug,' she said scornfully.

Robin Klein

The brave little toaster

There were hair dryers and four-speed bicycles, water heaters and wind-up toys that would all have gone on working for years and years with just the slightest maintenance. Instead, they'd be sent to city dump! You could hear their hopeless sighs and crazed murmurings rising from every dark mound around, a ghastly medley that seemed to swell louder every moment as more and more of the forlorn, abandoned objects became conscious of the energetic new appliances in their midst.

'You will never, never, never get away,' whispered a mad old cassette player in a cracked voice. 'No, never! You will stay here like all the rest of us and rust and crack and turn to dust. And never get away.'

'We will, though,' said the toaster. 'Just you wait and see.'

But how? That was the problem the toaster had to solve without further delay.

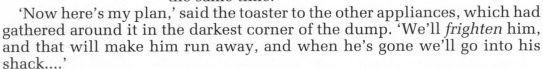

Now the surest way to solve any problem is to think about it, and that's just what the toaster did. It thought with the kind of total, all-out effort you have to give to get a bolt off that's rusted on to a screw. At first the bolt won't budge, not the least bit, and the wrench may slip loose, and you begin to doubt that any amount of trying is going to accomplish your purpose. But you keep at it, and use a dab of solvent if there's any on hand, and eventually it starts to give. You're not even sure but you think so. And then, what do you know, it's off! You've done it! That's the way the toaster thought, and at last, because it thought so hard, it thought of a way they could escape from the pirate and rescue the radio at the same time.

'Now here's my plan,' said the toaster to the other appliances, which had gathered around it in the darkest corner of the dump. 'We'll *frighten* him, and that will make him run away, and when he's gone we'll go into his shack....'

'Oh, no, I *couldn't* do that,' said the blanket with a shiver of dread.

'We'll go into his shack,' the toaster insisted calmly, 'and get the radio and put it inside the baby buggy and get in ourselves, all except the Hoover, of course, which will hightail it out of this place just as fast as it can.'

'But won't the gate be locked?' the lamp wanted to know. 'It is now.'

'No, because the pirate will have to unlock it to get out himself, and he'll be too frightened to remember to lock it behind him.'

'It's a very good plan,' said the Hoover, 'but what I don't understand is – *how* are we going to frighten him?'

'Well, what are people afraid of the most?'

'Getting run over by a steamroller?' the Hoover guessed.

'No. Scarier than that.'

'Moths?' suggested the blanket.

'No.'

'The dark,' declared the lamp with conviction.

'That's close,' said the toaster. 'They're afraid of ghosts.'

'What are ghosts?' demanded the Hoover.

'Ghosts are people who are dead, only they're also sort of alive.'

'Don't be silly,' said the lamp. 'Either they *are* dead or they aren't.'

'Yes,' the blanket agreed. 'It's as simple as ON and OFF. If you're ON, you can't be OFF, and vice versa.'

'*I* know that, and *you* know that, but people don't seem to. People say they know that ghosts don't exist but they're afraid of them anyhow.'

'No one can be afraid of something that doesn't exist,' the Hoover huffed.

'Don't ask me how they do it,' said the toaster. 'It's what they call a paradox. The point is this – people are afraid of ghosts. And so *we're* going to pretend to be one.'

'How?' asked the Hoover skeptically.

'Let me show you. Stoop down. Lower. Wrap your cord around my cord. Now – lift me up.....'

After an hour's practice of pretending to be a ghost, they decided they were ready. Carefully, so that the other appliances wouldn't fall off, the old Hoover trundled toward the window of the shack. The toaster, where it was balanced atop the handle of the vacuum, was just able to see inside. There on a table between a stack of unwashed dishes and the pirate's ring of keys was the poor captive radio, and there, in dirty striped pajamas, getting ready to go to bed, was the pirate.

'Ready?' the toaster whispered.

The blanket, which was draped over the vacuum in a roughly ghostlike shape with a kind of hood at the top through which the toaster was able to peer out, adjusted its folds one last time. 'Ready,' the blanket replied.

'Ready?' the toaster asked again.

For just a moment the lamp, where it was hidden halfway down the handle of the Hoover, turned itself on and then, quickly, off. The bulb it had taken from the socket in the ceiling of the pickup truck had only half the wattage it was used to, and so its beam of light was noticeably dimmer – just enough to make the blanket give off the faintest yellowish glow.

'Then let's start haunting,' said the toaster.

That was the signal the Hoover had been waiting for.

'Whoo!' groaned the Hoover in its deepest, most quivery voice. 'Whoo!'

The pirate looked up with alarm. 'Who's there?' he demanded.

'Whoo-oo!' the Hoover continued.

'Whoever you are, you'd better go away.'

'Whoo-oo-oo!'

Cautiously the pirate approached the window from which the groaning seemed to issue.

Upon receiving a secret electric signal from the toaster, the vacuum crept quietly alongside the shack to where they would be out of sight from the window.

'Whoo...' breathed the Hoover in the barest of whispers. 'Whoo... whoo-oo....'

'Who's out there?' the pirate demanded, pressing his nose against the pane of glass and peering into the outer darkness. 'You'd better answer me. Do you hear?'

In answer the Hoover made a strangling, gurgling, gaspy sound that sounded frightening even if you knew it was only the Hoover doing it. By now the pirate, who didn't have any idea what this mysterious groaning might be, had got into a considerable state of nerves. When you live all alone in the city dump you don't expect to hear strange noises just outside your window in the middle of the night. And if you were also a bit superstitious, as pirates tend to be....

'All right then – if you won't say who you are, I'm going to come out there and find out!' He lingered yet a while before the window, but at last, when no reply was forthcoming, the pirate pulled on his trousers and then got into his boots. 'I'm warning you!' he called out, though not in a tone that could be called threatening.

Still there was no reply. He took up his key ring from where it lay on the table beside the radio. He went to the door.

He opened it.

'Now!' said the toaster, signalling secretly to the blanket along its electric cord.

'I can't,' said the blanket, all atremble. 'I'm too afraid.'

'You *must*!'

'I mustn't: it's against the rules.'

'We discussed all that before, and you *promised*. Now hurry – before he gets here!'

With a shudder of trepidation the blanket did as it was bidden. There was a tear in its side where it had been pierced by a branch on the night it was blown up into the tree. The lamp was hiding just behind this rent. As the pirate appeared around the corner of the shack, the blanket twitched the torn fabric aside.

The pirate stopped short in his tracks when he saw the shrouded figure before him.

'Whoo-oo!' groaned the Hoover one last time.

At this cue the lamp turned itself on. Its beam slanted up through the hole in the blanket right into the pirate's face.

When the lamp lit up, the pirate stared at the figure before him with the utmost horror. What he saw that was so frightening was his own features reflected in the toaster's mottled chrome. And as he had been a very wicked person from his earliest youth, his face had taken on that special kind of ugliness that only very evil people's faces acquire. Seeing such a face grimacing at him from this strange hooded figure, what was the pirate to suppose but that he had come upon the most dangerous kind of ghost, the kind that understands exactly who we are and knows all the wrong things we've done and intends to punish us for them. From such ghosts even grown-up pirates will flee in terror. Which is exactly what the pirate did.

As soon as he was gone, the appliances rushed into the pirate's shack and rescued the joyful radio. Then before the pirate could return they scrambled into the baby buggy, and the old Hoover drove off with them as fast as its wheels would revolve.

Thomas Disch

The Edge

The Edge is a long sandstone ridge to the west of Kinver in Staffordshire. Its woods of oak and birch are beautiful in autumn. In August its sandy slopes are rich with golden fronds of seeded grass and purple heather where adders bask sleepily, hidden, on hot afternoons. If you go there on a quiet day when it isn't crowded with dogs and people, you can still feel the old magic of the place. More so in winter, when dead bracken is rigid with frost, or trees shrouded in mist.

There is a story that once upon a time a giant lived in a cave on the Edge. No one knows if the giant really existed, but the caves are still there. They were lived in until the 1960s and they all have magical-sounding names. There's Nanny's Rock – people believed Nanny to be a witch because she kept dried snake skins in her cave and brewed potions from herbs – then there's Holy Austin Rock, where a friar lived, and Vale's Rock and Gibraltar Rock, although how they came by their names I don't know.

The caves were easily made into homes as the soft red stone could be easily cut. In Victorian times Holy Austin Rock had six cottages in it on two levels. The ones below were simply hewn in the rock and had doors and windows added. But the two storey cottages above had brick-built fronts, tiled roofs, and gable ends. These houses, still remote from the village and

only reached by a steep flight of steps, were comfortable and warm inside. They had plastered, limewashed walls with alcoves cut into them for cupboards and shelves. Their floors were laid with red quarry tiles and they all had fireplaces or a blacklead range.

Outside were neat, well-kept gardens. The soil for these gardens had to be carried up by the residents on their shoulders. Outside too was a deep-water well, which was used by all the rock dwellers. Ann Edwards, a washerwoman, lived at number 2. Other residents included agricultural labourers, a besom (broom) maker and a mole-catcher. Labourers from the village iron works had lived there too at one time, but they had long since gone. Some families lived in Holy Austin for generations, proud of their unique and hard-won homes.

Nanny's Rock was quite different from Holy Austin Rock. It was more remote, hidden on the other side of the Edge and it could only be reached after a steep and dangerous climb. It had openings cut in it for doors and windows, and the 'Devil's Chimney' cut through the rock, but it is still simply a cavern. Before Nanny lived there it was known as 'Meg-o'-Fox-hole'. Margaret of the fox earth died in 1617, and her name is entered in the parish register. Nanny, the 'witch', was a much more recent inhabitant. No one knows how or when she died – she simply disappeared.

Jack Leyland, on the other hand, is still remembered today. He was a first-class besom maker, and was the last tenant to live in the caves. He lived at Vale's Rock until 1960.

Less healthy than the caves on the Edge were the Rocks of Gibralter. These lay alongside the canal wharf and were small and damp. If you were an iron-worker, or a cargo loader for the narrowboats, you could rent a cave for yourself and family for a shilling a week. But by living there you risked sickness and many children died of diseases such as smallpox. Even the caves themselves have now long since crumbled from the wet.

Some of the caves on the Edge still have their brick-built fronts with the occasional door or window-frame intact. You can also still see the blackened marks of soot on chimneys, part brick, part rock. If you climb up the Holy Austin now you can look out over the village of Kinver, the wooded valleys and countryside below. The sand is cold under your feet. The dying sun casts strange shadows through the holes sculpted in the soft red stone shaped by time, weather and people.

It's then that you think of the people who used to live here. Of how they looked through these same windows, watching the twilight gather in the winter dusk, and how they lit their lamps and fires, tended their summer gardens and drew water from the well. Ghosts of not so long ago.

And the giant? Well, local legend says he quarrelled with another giant who lived in Samson's Cave. Samson's Cave is two miles away, in the next village. Our giant was so angry that he hurled a huge stone from the topmost point of the Edge at his fleeing enemy. It landed in a field somewhere near here. Although no one has ever found the stone, it is mentioned in the county records as the 'Bolt Stone'.

When a storm is raging over Kinver and when lightning splits the sky and the angry giant's voice is heard again, it's probably wise to stay indoors!

Ann Bonner

Index of Authors

Index of Themes

Index of Titles